A catalogue record for this book is available from the National Library of Ireland and the British Library.

ISBN 978-1-5272-1698-3

First Published in Ireland in 2017 by

Eninserv Limited

Shankill, Co. Dublin, Ireland

www.eninserv.com

Errors and Omissions

Dedication

To Natalia,

Without your patience and support, this book could never have happened.

Chapters

Preface

I have always been interested in technology and definitely could be described as a 'gadgets man'. I can thank one of my older brothers for introducing me to electronics when I was in my early teens. This relationship with electrons has grown, expanded and diversified over more than 35 years. It has introduced me to many aspects of technology and engineering and somewhere through it all, I have managed to stay conscious of the need for sustainable commerce in every good idea. Without good business, even the most fascinating invention just won't gain traction (although somebody will probably give me an example that proves the rule).

My introduction to Electric Vehicles really started in 2011 when I joined an electric vehicle project team for my then employer ESB, the Electricity Supply Board in Ireland. I was aware of Electric Vehicles before this time and I even thought I new something about them. This is about the right time to acknowledge Senan McGrath, my then boss. Senan was more than a boss, but very much a mentor as I found my way around a new industry. He was a mind of information both technically and politically, never missing an opportunity to bring me up to speed or into the loop with all that was happening in this exciting new world.

I soon discovered how much was happening in this industry that I wasn't previously aware of. In 2011, it was becoming obvious that the new introduction of an old technology showed real potential. Standards were being developed with mass deployment in mind, however behind the scenes everyone was vying for position to secure their slice of the action. Energy Utilities saw the technology as a potential new market, while the vehicle manufacturers saw this market as an automotive domain and desired to grow its relationship with the customer into areas such as fuel provision and any other streams of income. On another side, in this ever more connected world, the ICT and telecoms industries saw potential for taking their percentage off the top of all of these data transactions. And of course lets not forget the many companies far removed from the traditional automotive industry that decided to develop or collaborate in the development of autonomous electric vehicles.

So, I'm probably no different because I am trying to sell you a book on the topic. Well, I am confident and hope you will find this up to date publication, useful and worth the modest cover price. As an EV owner and driver, a technology developer, entrepreneur and electrical practitioner all wrapped into one, I hope I can answer most of the questions which exist or may soon exist in your head as you start to think about how you will interact with Electric Vehicles. I also believe my views are broad enough to consider the standpoints of most of the wide variety of stakeholders in this arena. If by some stretch of the imagination (I jest), I have missed something; please feel free to let me know.

Conscious of who my audience might be, I have developed the chapters with the EV curious or novice in mind. If you are seeking in-depth scientific explanations, you are in the wrong place. I aim to give readers a good understanding of the topics, introducing physics only to the extent required to understand the principles of the chapter. As you browse or read this book in detail, there will be some chapters of more immediate interest than others. I have tried to structure the book both logically for those intending to read from cover to cover, but also to facilitate those who would like to cherry pick the chapters they are most interested in, skipping over one or two along the way (big mistake). You should be able to jump in on any chapter and not necessarily read all preceding chapters.

I really hope you find what you are looking for in this book and a whole lot more.

Chapter 1

Is This Really Happening?

This is one of the most common questions I have heard over the last number of years, although it is definitely becoming less frequent as reality dawns and people become more and more aware of the progress being made across the world. If I had a Euro for every time I have heard "Electric Vehicles won't become widespread in my generation" or "Yeah, but I'll always have my gasoline car", I'd be a wealthy man.

Yes, Electric Vehicles are here and now and for the long haul. What about hydrogen, I hear that guy at the back ask. Well it may gain market share in the future, however I am firmly of the belief that progress in Battery Electric Vehicles (BEV's) has taken a significant lead, ensuring that it will be many years before hydrogen becomes dominant, if ever.

So what are the deciding factors?

First there is Price: Over the last couple of years the cost of new electric vehicles has fallen considerably. This has meant that when you need to decide between a combustion engine vehicle and an electric vehicle, price is no longer an issue. Furthermore, if you typically purchase pre-owned vehicles, the market has started to pick up, as early adopters have traded in their vehicles to get the latest model. Second-hand prices are also in the ballpark of similar combustion engine vehicles. This allows us to move swiftly on to the next deciding factor.

Driving range: Driving range or autonomy was a major stumbling block in the early years of the 21st century revival of electric vehicles. Back in 2010, the pre-production vehicles that I managed could only travel 60km (38 miles) before needing to be topped up. This was certainly a problem at the time and gave vehicles a well-deserved tag line of "city car". However by 2011, the production vehicles were delivering real driving ranges of 100km (62 miles) and these distances have been increasing steadily since. In 2017 economy & medium class vehicles are now able to achieve 200km (125 miles), with larger batteries available and on the horizon, allowing even greater driving ranges. We have definitely left the tag line "city car" behind and while 'sales rep' mileage is still not practical for a year or two in most economy cars, the majority of commuter and social journeys are easily managed.

Charge point availability: Range anxiety was the buzz phrase of early electric vehicle critics. Yes it existed and yes it was a real issue, however the reality of range anxiety today is more about information availability than charging availability. At the same time a combination of bias or ill informed journalists and critics are misleading the

public with out-dated information. Fake News I Say! :-
)............

Brand Loyalty: The number of EV makes & models has increased. Almost every brand is now offering electric vehicles and if there are any brands still lagging behind, it won't be long before they take steps to catch up. In fact as I write this, it seems like there is a competition to see who can get the best headlines from their EV announcements. BMW, VW, Toyota, Tesla and Volvo are all in the game. Even Nissan who have been notable leaders in the area, have announced their new Nissan Leaf with more features and more driving range. If you think that EV's are still in the realms of one or two niche makers, then look again, you will only need to look to your current supplier.

Speed of Recharge: The speed of charging is increasing and we are soon to see high performance charging that will allow approximately 450km (280 miles) of driving in less than 15 minutes of charging. Charging overnight at home doesn't always require a high speed of charge. After all, you are likely to be plugged in for many hours regardless of what charge you require. When you are out and about, you can access fast charging, which would typically give you about 100km (60 miles) in 20 minutes. The new High Performance Charging promises to knock this out of the ballpark.

Lets look a little beyond electric vehicles. There is something truly important happening. Many of you will be familiar with the Fire Triangle, which illustrates that you need Oxygen, Fuel and Heat to create and maintain a fire. Today I believe we have another triangle. The Sustainable Mobility Triangle looks at the factors of Renewable Energy, Battery Storage and Electric Mobility.

Each of these areas has entered the phase where they have become far more affordable and far more efficient than the technology of past years. Homes and commercial buildings are increasingly adding solar or wind generation. Battery prices have dropped significantly and the life expectancy has increased. Nissan and Tesla have both developed energy storage products, which utilizes vehicle battery technology, making building energy storage a more economical proposition. Finally as we are learning, Electric Vehicles have also hit the sweet spot, where price and life expectancy are ripe for the picking.

Reaching the age of maturity for each of these technologies is good news. But more importantly, the convergence of all three, offers a path to truly sustainable mobility, where the vehicle can be fuelled by clean energy and where the battery whether in the home or in the vehicle can assist in the clean up of our more universal electricity consumption.

Chapter 2

All Electric Or Hybrid?

There are a number of variations on electric vehicle technology. In this section, I will point out the main variants, offering a simplified definition and discussing some of the pros & cons of each. If you are choosing between an all electric and a hybrid vehicle, this chapter will help you reach a decision that works for you.

First lets be clear about what we are talking about:

BEV – A 'Battery Electric Vehicle' is a vehicle that uses a battery as the sole means of energy storage for the propulsion of the vehicle. A BEV does not have either a gasoline generator or propulsion engine. It is driven purely by an electric motor with battery energy storage.

PEV – A 'Plug-in Electric Vehicle' is any electric vehicle that can be plugged into a charge point to allow recharging of the traction battery. These can include all battery electric vehicles as well as plug-in hybrid vehicles.

PHEV – A Plug-in Hybrid Electric Vehicle is a vehicle that utilises both an Internal Combustion Engine (ICE) and electric motor(s) to propel the vehicle. The battery can be regenerated either by the ICE, the motion of the wheels or by plugging the vehicle into a charge point when parked. Plugging into a charge point (when available) constitutes the most efficient use of energy and is cleaner for the environment.

REEV – A Range Extender Electric Vehicle is a vehicle, which is driven solely by an electric motor. In addition to the battery which stores electrical energy supplied by plugging in the vehicle, a small gasoline generator is also fitted to the vehicle. This generator is used to recharge the battery and cannot provide direct propulsion to the vehicle. Using gasoline to fuel a generator in an REEV is still more efficient than using the same gasoline to fuel an ICE for propulsion.

And lets not forget.......

HEV – A 'Hybrid Electric Vehicle' is a vehicle propelled by a combination of electricity and gasoline. Both an ICE engine and electric motor(s) are connected to the drive train of the vehicle. The electric battery however, is only charged by the ICE, the motion of the wheels or a combination of both. There is no charging connector and therefore the vehicle cannot be recharged by power from a household or public charge point.

It is worth noting that technically a HEV can refer to either a plug-in hybrid or a non-plug-in hybrid vehicle. Normally the term is reserved for a non-plug-in vehicle.

Lets talk about the pros & cons, what do you need to know when you are considering each of these.

The key talking points when discussing the pros & cons of various EV configurations consist of:

- **Vehicle cost**

Electric vehicles historically have had the label 'expensive' attached to them. While this stigma still resonates in the minds of many, it is far less relevant today than it was back in 2010. However we still need to remember that if we want everything we must be prepared to pay for it. The question is; do we need everything?.... Often, the answer is No.

When we purchase a BEV, all our investment is channelled into the battery and electric motor. When we use the vehicle, we are gaining the maximum use of the investment, each and every time we travel in it. Should we decide to choose a hybrid vehicle, we are investing in two technologies. When we drive the vehicle, we are often only using one of the technologies and not both.

When it comes to cost, we need to remember that if you want more, it will cost more. So, when we buy a hybrid, we should be paying much more for the vehicle. In reality, the cost of a hybrid is not that much more than a straight BEV. So what gives? The answer is the battery size. Hybrid vehicles are typically equipped with a much smaller battery than a BEV, therefore they will travel shorter distances on electric power before swapping back to gasoline.

- **Driving range**

The driving range or autonomy of a vehicle is mainly influenced by the amount of fuel stored on-board. Fuel can be either in the form of electricity or gasoline. When you choose a hybrid vehicle, you are typically gaining driving autonomy due to the combustion engine and therefore will require fewer stops to refuel than a BEV. This is very convenient, particularly when you drive long distances. We should however remember that the electric autonomy of the vehicle is far less in a hybrid than a straight BEV. This should be remembered as it impacts the cost of fuel and efficiencies of the vehicle.

We should also consider that autonomy of BEV's has increased greatly since they reappeared on the market back in 2010. In keeping with my intension to be balanced in my portrayals, I will only refer to realistic driving ranges, I will not partake in the grossly unrepresentative brochure figures. In fairness to the vehicle manufacturers these brochure stats are based on European Drive Cycles and similar jurisdictional standards. They are therefore unrepresentative across the industry as a whole. So back to topic, ... lets generally agree that the overall driving range is not an issue for hybrid vehicles, offering autonomy greater than 700km (440 miles). Furthermore the time required to refuel is short and wide-scale availability of gasoline refuelling stations is undisputed.

BEV's on the other hand come with driving ranges from 100km (62 miles) up to approximately 500km (320 miles) and this figure is growing. Needless to say, the cost increases with the autonomy, so you will need to be realistic about your specification requirements. The typical economy class vehicle available on the market today offers 120km (75 miles) or greater. This is far in excess of the typical suburban-urban daily commute. With the exception of many professionals who travel large distances each day while fulfilling their work schedule, most of the rest of us, look at the occasional weekend or vacation journey as the benchmark for driving requirements. I would argue that the frequency of this requirement and the availability of alternative means of travel are as much if not more important.

Before we move on to the next topic, I think it is worth stressing that the electrical autonomy of a PHEV is very small, with real driving ranges of between 20 and 60km (13-37 miles) depending on the vehicle model. It is also my experience that PHEV's tend to demonstrate the greatest deviation between brochure autonomy and real life autonomy.

- **Energy efficiency**

The topic of energy efficiency could take us in many different directions. Chassis weight, aerodynamics, driving styles and many more, however for purpose of this assessment we will stick to the topic as it relates to PEV's.

Carrying around battery weight that is underutilised is counterproductive when it comes to energy efficiency. Equally, carrying an ICE as well as an electric motor and battery has a negative impact on efficiency. Before we increase the specification we need to ask ourselves, why and how often will we need it?

We should also ask ourselves; how disciplined are we? In the case of a BEV, we will soon learn to be disciplined. If we don't plug in at night, we will soon run out of power and be inconvenienced by the time then required to recharge. On the other hand, with a PHEV, we can forget to plug-in as often as we like with no repercussions...... Well actually, there are. You may still be able to get into your vehicle and drive, however every time you miss an opportunity to recharge, you are impacting negatively on the energy efficiency of the vehicle. Now you are using more expensive and less environmentally friendly fossil fuels to propel your vehicle and the battery that you are carrying around just for fun. If you don't take the opportunity to charge a PHEV, you would be much better of in a ICE vehicle with no electric drive.

- **Fuel cost**

The topic of fuel cost is important. With few, if any, exceptions, the cost of electricity is cheaper per km (mile) than that of petrol or diesel. When the purchase costs of EV's were greater, the time taken to see the real economic benefits of an EV was longer, however today that time is almost immediate. There is often an initial sting, when a householder sees an increase in their electricity bill, until they realise that this is far less than the decrease in their petrol or diesel bill. Likewise, those, of us, who have benefitted from the availability of free services in the early days of EV's need to accept that EV charging is a commodity and we must pay a fair price for it.

The electricity providers in most regions offer two tariffs, peak or daytime and off-peak or night-time tariffs. In some regions, more tariff categories exist; in fact the likelihood is that there will be many more time of usage tariffs or even dynamic tariffs in the future. This offers us an opportunity to optimise when we charge our vehicles, allowing us to access the cheapest rates. In the simplest terms, we can charge at night at rates that are typically half of what we would pay during the daytime. Whether you choose a BEV or a PHEV, you should try to access the cheapest fuel cost. Many vehicles have timers built in, which allow us to schedule when charging will begin.

- **Charging speeds**

For many users, the time taken to charge is very important. The chapter 'Refuelling Your EV' will look at this in more detail, however for now we will compare the refuelling experience for a PEV.

The fossil fuel experience is quite straight forward. Just pull up to the fuel pump at a convenient station and refuel. The total time from start to finish is approximately 5-6 minutes. You will have gained approximately 700km (440 miles) of driving range.

Circumstances around electric refuelling can vary. Firstly, the ultimate for many drivers is to refuel when you are sleeping; overnight charging takes no time from our busy schedules and is generally cheaper. After this, most vehicles come with a fast charge or rapid charge (the terminology can depend on your jurisdiction) and a slow (normal) charge. A slow charge tends to suit occasions where you are intending to park for one or more hours. Typically in 1 hour you can gain approximately 40km (25 miles) of autonomy. Some vehicles can gain more and some less.

On the other hand, when you are en route to a destination and you need to recharge, then you will need to rely on a fast/rapid charger. These chargers typically deliver approximately 100 km (62.5 miles) in approximately 30 minutes. Most BEV's are equipped with fast/rapid charge capability, however the majority of PHEV's do not offer this function. The logic here, is that the PHEV will just refill with gasoline when it is en route, so slower charging is more effective.

- **Vehicle size**

The size of the vehicle required is very important when choosing an EV. Currently BEV's are primarily focused on small to medium size vehicles. Larger passenger vehicles are so far, less frequent in BEV's. This is however changing, so keep your eyes open.

PHEV's are available across both small and larger vehicles. So when you need a larger passenger vehicle PHEV's generally offer the best options, however don't forget the point about regular long distance driving, sometimes a straight ICE is more economical.

Commercial vans are now reaching BEV maturity. There are a number of makes and models available and the sizes can vary, up to and beyond a 10 tonne truck.

Now lets look at the various types in isolation.

BEV - The Battery Electric Vehicle offers the best

option for fuel efficiency and fuel cost. BEV's tend to be very comfortable and very quiet. The limiting factor of a BEV is the battery size. In fact, these days this is less of a limit than most people realise. In truth, you need to ask yourself, where do I drive? and do I need to travel long distances very often? If we consider that a BEV tends to have upwards of 120km (75 mile) range, then it will suit a lot of people for all their driving. Moreover it will suit an even greater number of people who only occasionally drive longer distances. We need to remember that if you only occasionally need the longer range, you still have the option to stop for a fast/rapid charge. Lets face it, the small additional time will be well paid for by the cost efficiencies gained all the rest of the year. Another factor to consider is whether this is the only car in the family. For example, if your spouse or partner also drives, you may at least be able to keep one vehicle as a BEV and still have a greater range capability in the second vehicle. However, if the BEV is expected to regularly require recharging for long distance driving, then the time required may become over burdensome.

HEV - Hybrid Electric Vehicle's offer a small efficiency over an ICE vehicle. The efficiency is most noticeable when the majority of the driving is urban. A HEV still uses petrol or diesel to refuel the vehicle and cannot plug in to an electrical charge point. The fuel efficiency and environmental impact of the HEV is less than a PHEV and far less again than a BEV. My opinion is that the developments on EV technology are fast eating away at any remaining advantages of the tradition HEV. It might be more appropriate to refer to them as an efficient combustion engine vehicle.

PHEV - Plug-in Hybrid Electric Vehicles offer more efficiencies than a HEV but less than an EV. The advantage is that when you are on longer journeys, you do not need to stop and recharge as often as in a BEV. You must however ensure that you take every opportunity possible to recharge on electricity rather than using the fossil fuel alternative. This will ensure you maximize the potential of the vehicle. As with HEV, I believe that progress in BEV autonomy will fast strip away the benefits of a PHEV. There will be no practical need to carry around a heavy and inefficient ICE in vehicles.

REEV - The little discussed Range Extender Electric Vehicle actually offers a very nice middle ground for many people. Similar to the PHEV, I believe it will eventually be overtaken by the BEV due to autonomy gains, however there are a couple of clear advantages over the PHEV. REEV's tend to offer battery sizes in line with the BEV and therefore the distances achievable on electric power are much greater than a PHEV. Furthermore the efficiency of fuelling a generator with fossil fuels rather than an engine to propel the vehicle is a second clear winner. Finally the additional weight of the generator versus the engine also adds to the advantage of an REEV over the PHEV.

Chapter 3

So, What About The Battery?

The future of batteries, life expectancy, cost, safety, second life usage and reconditioning, are all topics I have heard debated over the last number of years. As with many other EV topics it is an area rife with bad information. In this chapter, I will attempt to give you a fair and realistic view of where things are at. My knowledge of the topic from an EV perspective is up to scratch, however I am not a qualified battery chemist, so don't expect a science lesson.

The battery is the part of the vehicle that stores the electric energy until we are ready to use it. Battery is a term, which refers to a package containing a number of cells that store energy. These cells are connected together to bring the overall package to a size that can be used by an appliance, in this case an electric vehicle. From now on we will avoid the term 'cell' and stick to batteries.

Current EV batteries are based on one of a number of Lithium variations. Lithium-Ion Manganese Oxide (LMO) and Lithium Nickel Manganese Cobalt Oxide (NMC) are two of the most common types. Depending on the use of the battery, there will be many trade offs between, cost, weight, energy density and potentially hazardous materials. For an electric vehicle, manufacturers need to have a safe battery, which is as light as possible, storing as much energy as possible and cheap to install in the vehicle. Another element is the number of charge-discharge cycles the battery can give before it becomes practically useless; after all we don't want to be replacing the battery too often or at all. Battery technologies have improved leaps and bounds, particularly in the last 20 years. When I look back to my first mobile phone, it had a massive battery, which stored a small amount of energy. It was heavy and it discharged in a short amount of time, even if the phone was switched off. The battery in my phone or laptop today, is a fraction of the size and can store more energy. Furthermore, if I leave my phone switched off, it doesn't empty the battery for a very long time. This leads me to one of the most frequently asked questions:

If I leave an EV parked for a few days, will the battery discharge?

No, not really. One of the characteristics of Lithium based batteries, particularly those used in electric vehicles is that they have a very low rate of self-discharge. I have left vehicles parked for 2 or 3 weeks, when I returned, the vehicle displayed a fill level within 1% of where I had left it. Some manufacturers of EV's recommend that if you are going to leave a vehicle in storage for more than a couple of weeks, you should leave it plugged in to the charge point. This was supposed to allow the battery cells to stay balanced and maintain the health of the battery. By the way, you have two batteries in an EV, the auxiliary 12V battery still exists similar to an ICE vehicle. The auxiliary battery is typically a lead acid battery and older batteries may discharge over long periods, particularly when the weather is cold. Should this happen, you will not be able to start your vehicle as the contactor which connects the traction battery to the vehicle will not operate. This is actually no different to that of a combustion engine vehicle, as even with a full tank of fuel, these also, wouldn't start if the starter motor cannot turn.

What is the life expectancy of the battery?

I have heard figures from 5 years to 20 years quoted. In short, I tend to tell people, that >10 years is a reasonable expectation. While there are some instances of shorter battery life, these have typically been due to rough treatment of the battery. If you abuse it, it will die. In reality this depends on a number of factors. The number of charge-discharge cycles of a battery differs with the battery chemistry. Closely tied to this is the depth of discharge of the battery, in other words, how low is my battery when I recharge it. The deeper the discharge the fewer cycles the battery has. Battery temperature is another significant factor. In general terms, this is managed by the vehicles battery management system, however there are influencing factors sometimes outside its control. High power discharge, i.e.

heavy acceleration can cause temperatures to rise, this is not an issue in moderation, however, if you are racing hard and then recharging fast on a regular basis, it can take its toll on the battery. Regular high ambient temperatures also take their toll. Believe me, this is not an issue where I live, however if you live in Nevada or the Middle East or some similarly hot area, this can be a factor. I do know that the vehicle manufacturers often offer tailored features for particular regions and were discussing fitting advanced cooling systems in some jurisdictions.

When is the battery at the end of its useful life?

The rule of thumb is 70% of the original capacity. When the battery has degraded to approximately 70% of its day one storage, it is considered to be at the end of its useful life for automotive traction. We will look at what happens that remaining good battery later. In some vehicles battery health is indicated on the dashboard display, in other cases you may need the service report from the vehicle. The vehicles that I have most experience with, have a coarse 12 point indication on the dashboard. I have seen many vehicles with >60,000km (37,500 miles) still showing all 12 segments, this tells me that they are still above 91% on the health scale.

How big are the batteries?

When most people ask this question they tend to mean, how much energy do they store or how far will it take me. Battery sizes are increasing with the introduction of new generations of vehicles. Some of the early production vehicles in 2010 were as small as 16kWh's. The Nissan Leaf was first introduced with a 24kWh battery, later offering an option for a 30kWh and now with a 40kWh battery as standard. Battery sizes up to and beyond 100kWh's are available, however the larger you buy, the more it will cost, so ask yourself how often will I use it? The sizes, I am quoting here are typical for BEV's. If you are looking at a PHEV, the batteries will be much smaller, often only 6 or 7kWh. Combine this with the weight of a combustion engine and you can imagine that PHEV's with small batteries don't travel that far on electric power.

Can I carry a spare battery?

While it is technically possible, it is generally considered impractical. Batteries are heavy and costly, so you probably won't want to be carrying around a spare battery just in case. Remember also, that the spare battery will need to be connected to the vehicle to allow transfer of energy to the traction battery. This cannot be done while the vehicle is moving and will need a controller with all the connections and protocols to allow transfer. In reality, if you have the need for more battery storage on a regular basis, you should be looking at purchasing a larger battery option with the vehicle.

Companies such as JTM Power offer the EV Rescue. This type of product is intended for roadside rescue vans or car showrooms and workshops. Carrying one in the rear of your car might be a little much.

How far will my battery take me?

This depends on the battery size or capacity. It also depends on my driving habits and even the weather. We will get to the battery capacity soon, first we will consider driving habits. Just like an ICE, if you are heavy on the pedal, you are going to use more fuel. Fast acceleration, driving a constant high speeds and heavy breaking will impact negatively on your energy usage. Many vehicles offer ECO mode and similar driving style features. Driving in ECO tends to limit the amount of acceleration from stop, therefore saving energy. In reality, if we are driving in an urban area, we don't need to accelerate heavily from the traffic lights, just to brake heavily again in 100m at the next set of signals. My driving history report allows me to see my energy usage. I typically use between 16 and 17 kWh's per 100km (62 miles), so with a 24kWh battery, I achieve an average of 140km (88 miles) on a charge.

Can I upgrade to a larger battery later?

At the time of writing this, I would have to say no. I would also venture that if history of other appliances is anything to go by, we won't be able to do it in the foreseeable future either. There are a number of reasons for this opinion; In honesty, its probably not good business for the vehicle manufacturer, after all they would prefer we change the vehicle. However there are other practical reasons, which would reinforce the argument. As with mobile phones, a battery for one model device is not always the same for another. Greater energy storage often means larger batteries and these may not fit in the space provided. But I hear you ask, what about new chemistries with higher energy densities? Well different chemistries tend to have different voltage and temperature characteristics and this brings us to the issue of battery management software. The original battery management system is unlikely to be suitable for the new battery.

What will happen the battery when it reaches its end of life?

There are a number of possible options for when the EV battery loses it's *Va Va Voom,* however as this generation of EV batteries still haven't really reached retiring age, most of the expected options haven't found their market space yet.

One of the options is battery replacement. This option would mean taking out an old battery and replacing it with a brand new one. I can just imagine the cringe as you thing about the cost. Well first of all, the cost of batteries is dropping, however the old battery still has value in a second or subsequent life. I don't see this as a likely option, however it is an option.

Battery repair is another option. In this case, the service centre would connect the battery to a diagnostics tool and find which of the modules have reached a point where they drag down the battery health. These modules would then be replaced possibly adding another 3-5 years to the vehicle life, at a fraction of the cost of a new battery.

A third option would be repair exchange. In this option, the battery of circa 70% health, would be replaced with a reconditioned battery, this reconditioned battery would be certified, offering a defined state of health, lets say 95%. This would again add another 3-5 years on to the life of the vehicle, but with a much smaller investment than installing a brand new battery.

Next Generation Batteries

Battery technology has evolved and improved significantly over the years and particularly in our generation. Lead Acid batteries are no longer the only technology and while they still have some uses due to their relative low cost, the number of use cases has dropped from its previous high. Nickel Cadmium and Nickel Metal Hydrates have gained prominence in other areas. However for automotive traction batteries the chosen battery component is Lithium. Battery chemistry based on Lithium is where most if not all research is staying. Even in the few years since electric vehicle started to roll off the production lines of the big vehicle manufacturers, the battery chemistry has changed somewhat to improve the energy available and the experience of the driver. Batteries will continue to improve, however I am not holding my breath for the day when the improvements are so big, as to make obsolete all the existing vehicles.

The main considerations when developing new battery chemistry are:

- Safety

- Energy Density

- Cost

- Lifespan

- Raw materials

Safety

There has been much talk about battery safety, with stories of vehicles spontaneously combusting as well as batteries in mobile phones and even aeroplanes catching fire. Some of these events did happen in one form or another, however the details behind many were not always reported accurately. One of the articles I read, related to a battery at a test facility. I happen to know the people at the test facility, who informed me that the battery was undergoing a series of destructive tests, far exceeding regular usage. Let's face it: Headlines are the news!

None the less, there are very definite safety considerations which need to be considered when designing a battery and also producing them. For this reason there are a few chemical configurations for batteries, which may be electrically attractive but not remotely suitable for use in many applications including road vehicles.

Energy Density

When looking at any fuel for a mobile or portable application, you need to consider the energy density. It is one reason why petrol was so attractive, the ratio of energy to weight is good. For an electric vehicle, it is important to control the battery weight so as not to expend too much energy transporting the battery. Over the last couple of years, vehicle manufacturers have managed to pack higher energy batteries into the available space in the vehicles they produce. This is likely to improve further but not overnight and not massively.

Cost

This factor almost goes without saying. The cost of electric vehicle batteries has traditionally been the largest part of the cost of production. Since 2010 battery costs have dropped from $1000 per kWh to approximately $350 at present. It is expected that by 2025, costs will have further dropped to circa $200 per kWh. Before you start jumping up and down about the impact this drop in price may have on the value of your vehicle, it is worth remembering that so far, EV prices have been subsidised by the manufacturer and by government grants, which have allowed the vehicles to sell at an unnaturally low price. Therefore as the technology gets a bit cheaper, you can expect that the subsidies will fall away also, thus equalising the playing field.

Lifespan

The life expectancy of a battery is dependent on a number of factors mentioned already. Some battery chemistries are more susceptible to degradation from specific conditions than others, so the vehicle manufacturer most consider the use profiles, that can be expected for their products when they choose the battery chemistry. As an example, if you expect the charge-discharge profile of an electric vehicle to be fairly deep cycle, i.e, it discharges to a low state of charge and then recharges back up to a high state of charge on a regular basis, you would not choose a battery that degrades rapidly in a deep cycle mode. On the other hand, a battery used in building emergency lighting is likely to remain at a high state of charge, only discharging in the case of a power failure or during functional tests.

The focus on battery materials for next generation batteries will always need to remain conscious of the life expectancy under a specific use case. Bad choices in chemistry will leave the vehicle manufacturer open to warranty claims and reputational damage.

Raw Materials

The availability of raw materials is very important when choosing the type of battery, particularly when the battery is large as in the case of an electric vehicle. Battery manufacturers need to understand the expected availability of raw materials such as lithium, cobalt and all the other essential components. Their business depends on it, to ensure they can continue to manufacture products long into the future and at a cost that is affordable and sustainable. The cost projections for the key materials is crucial, as it's no use building a battery that is so expensive, nobody can reasonably afford it. Finally, the source of the raw material is also of high importance. As the key components are of a geological nature, they are sometimes only found in particular regions of the world. For this reason, the battery manufacturer needs to assess the possible side effects of political forces on the production and supply of the essential raw materials.

Natural resources

As we have just mentioned the consideration of raw material when designing a battery, lets continue to talk a little about the materials in a battery. The fact is, that Lithium is one of the smallest quantities in the making of a Lithium-ion battery. The four main parts of a battery are:

- The Enclosure or Housing

- The Cathode

- The Electrolyte

- The Anode

The *Enclosure* can be made from many different materials from alloys to plastics. These materials are chosen for strength, insulation and resistance to the chemicals in the battery itself. I won't focus any more on the enclosure as I believe it is not a pinch point when it comes to natural resources.

The *Cathode* in an EV battery is generally made from graphite. Over 60% of graphite production comes from China, however graphite is produced in many other countries such as Norway, India, Russia, Madagascar and Brazil. The cathode accounts for a large portion of the material in the overall battery.

The *Electrolyte* is the substance between the positive and negative electrodes of the battery. It is this substance that allows electrons to flow from one electrode to another when charging and discharging the battery. This is where the lithium comes in. The electrolyte is made up of lithium salts. There is however a fairly small amount of actual lithium here. Having researched through many different sources, I have calculated that the amount of actual lithium in a typical 24kWh battery is less than 2kg (<5lbs). To put this in perspective, the total battery would weigh almost 300kg (~650lbs). That's less than 1 per cent of the battery. 75% of lithium resources are found between Argentina, Bolivia and Chile.

The material used in the *Anode* varies with the make of the battery. Materials such as Manganese, Aluminium, Nickel and Cobalt are used either on their own or in a mixture. Manganese and aluminium are regarded as being in common supply. South Africa is the largest supplier of manganese, however it is available all over the world. The Philippines, Russia and Canada are amongst the largest producers of Nickel, however it is available in many parts of the world including Australia. Cobalt is probably the most critical of components. Therefore some battery manufacturers are avoiding it and probably all are looking at alternatives. The majority of production comes from the Democratic Republic of Congo, accounting for over 60% of cobalt mined in the world.

Will EV batteries be recycled?

The vehicle manufacturers producing the finished product are ultimately responsible for the battery when it reaches end of life. Immediately I think of the comments on forums and social media "Do you really think that the car companies are going to go around scrap heaps picking up batteries?

I certainly don't expect this to be the norm, however the car companies are clever, so I expect they approach the issue from a number of angles. Here are some examples: Can they avoid the issue? Can they defer the issue? Can they reduce the cost? Can they profit from the issue?

A strategy of avoidance is a very risky road indeed. Automotive companies are large with strong roots and they are not typically short sighted. Indeed they look further ahead than many industries. For this reason, they see the possible outcomes of being held accountable in a reactive manner rather than a proactive one.

Deferring the issue is far more attractive, particularly if it doesn't come with a high price tag and offers opportunities for reducing the financial impact as the world moves forward.

Second and subsequent uses of batteries after they are removed from the EV offer an opportunity to reduce the cost. The more use you make of the battery, the less it is likely to cost per use case to recycle the materials.

The ultimate case however; is profit. If the initial problem offers the opportunity for increased profits, then that is commercially speaking a nice problem to have. The opportunity exists to remove an electric vehicle battery from a vehicle and repackage most of it in a new form, to act as an energy buffer in homes, offices and even data centres.

It is no coincidence that most if not all vehicle manufacturers are putting a lot of effort into second life uses for the battery. In fact Nissan and Tesla already offer storage solutions for the building.

How effective is recycling?

I have been researching this subject since I first got serious about electric vehicles. When seeking high quality information you need to filter through the rubbish and segregate the biased viewpoints. I will try to keep this simple while setting out the key points to recycling, as I am aware of them.

There are two extremes of recycling with a number of hybrid options inserted in between. Smelting is a form of high temperature recycling where the organic material in the battery is burned off, while the valuable metals are refined and recycled. On the other end of the scale, you have direct recovery, where the battery grade material is recovered through chemical and physical processes. At the time of battery design, consideration should be afforded to the recycling process, as this would greatly assist in the practicality of separating the valuable metals.

The anode and cathode materials as well as the enclosure offer a very high degree of recyclability. In the case of smelting the electrolyte is used as a fuel and is burned off. In the case of direct recovery the electrolyte is removed and processed where the components are separated and can be reused in batteries and other uses.

It is important to remember that recycling of EV batteries is a relatively new industry and one that has yet to reach maturity. For this reason, the recycling processes today are certainly suboptimal and can be expected to develop over time.

Chapter 4

Electricity & Zero Emissions

One of the most common 'put downs' of Electric Vehicles is the old chestnut. "EV's are not zero emissions, the emissions are at the power station which generates the electricity". This is absolutely true but lets put some important points in context.

First of all BEV's should be referred to as Zero Tailpipe Emissions, rather than just zero emissions. This is far more accurate. I believe that the marketing of EV's got carried away when it coined the snappy 'Zero Emissions' slogan and in turn it has given ammunition to the petrol heads. The key message however is that EV's are cleaner than Internal combustion vehicles by a country mile. Even the recent drops in engine emissions across most makes and models have not caught up with EV's and at the same time the electricity generation is cleaning up also.

The principles of electricity as they apply to this topic are quite simple. We will assume that all our electricity is coming from the main electricity grid in our respective regions, not from home generation. In the majority, electricity is not stored like a water reservoir, rather the electricity generated, causes the flow of electrons along the cables and these electrons allow lights, machines, motors and other consumers to operate. Another point to remember is that all these electrons flow in the same cables, so it is physically not possible for me to guarantee that the electricity I consume comes from a particular source.

I can certainly have a contract with an energy supplier, which is based on the purchase of electricity from renewable sources such as wind or solar, but nobody is saying that these are the electrons delivered to my door. *(Note to the physics buffs, I do know that electrons move in the opposite direction to current flow… but lets keep this simple).*

To assess the true advantages of EV's against ICE's,

we do need to look at the source of the electricity used to power the vehicle. Power generation is fuelled in a number of ways. In some cases coal is burned to create electricity, in other cases the electricity generation is fuelled by oil, gas, biomass, wind, solar, wave and more. Coal, oil and gas are fossil fuels, which deplete the earth's natural resources and are the source of some of the carbon emissions that contribute to global warming. Biomass uses natural residues and waste as a fuel and therefore does not use our natural resources and is considered by some as a low carbon fuel.

Solar, wind and wave energy, use natural resources to generate energy, moreover, they do not generate any carbon emissions or green house gases. Just in case you thought I was going to overlook nuclear energy. Nuclear energy emits very low carbon amounts through the generation of electricity. There are many arguments against its use as a fuel, however it is widely accepted that it is a "clean" source of power from a carbons and Green House

Gases (GHG) perspective.

Energy Mix

Each country or electrical region has a unique profile of how it generates electricity. Some regions burn large amounts of coal, others are more focused on gas and some countries such as Norway have a high proportion of hydro generation. Understandably, countries tend to balance indigenous fuels with cheaper fuels. They may also want a mix of different fuels so as not to become over dependent on one in particular.

Different generation types, have different profiles, which often determines how they fit into the overall mix. Nuclear generators for example, tend to be constructed with large energy outputs. This means it may not fit into many smaller regions. These stations also run at a steady output and therefore cannot easily respond to fluctuations in demand.

Many consider wind generation as the ultimate model, as it is available all over the world and the 'fuel' is free. However the wind varies and the outputs of wind turbines follow these variations. As modern society requires energy on demand, wind could not be the sole form of generation.

The chart below, illustrates a typical mix of fuels. Don't worry about the actual numbers; these vary.

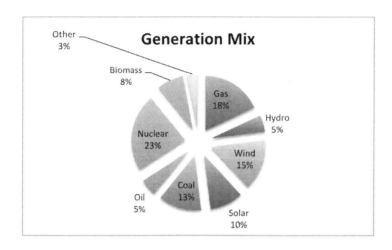

When we look at the equivalent emissions of electric vehicles, it will be dependent both on the region we live and even the time of day we refuel. For that reason, it would be impossible to set out definitive EV emission levels in this book.

What I have done below is set out what I consider a fair example of a real world scenario. What is clear however, is that unless your region is almost entirely dependent on coal as its fuel for electricity generation, EV's are still a cleaner option than driving an Internal Combustion Engine.

It is a goal of many developing societies to migrate electricity generation to 100% renewable sources over the coming years. Many countries have targets of 2050 or better to reach this holy grail of the electricity sphere. Until we reach a point of zero emissions from electricity generation, we will not be truly zero emissions from driving EV's. However even now there are significant benefits gained in emissions through adoption of electric vehicles.

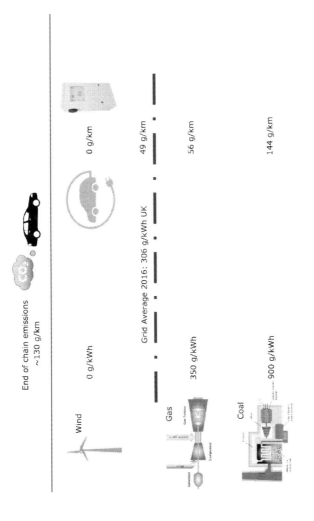

End of chain emissions
~130 g/km

0 g/km

0 g/km

Wind — 0 g/kWh

49 g/km

Grid Average 2016: 306 g/kWh UK

Gas — 350 g/kWh

56 g/km

Coal — 900 g/kWh

144 g/km

Chapter 5

Maybe I'll Wait

So far the electric vehicle adoption has followed the patterns of many previous technologies. Early adopters have given way to mainstream buyers. Having said this, I am still amazed at the lack of awareness amongst large numbers of drivers regarding how EV's can or can't work for them. Moreover it is probably out-dated information rather than no information that is causing the biggest barrier. A line I have heard too often is "Maybe I'll wait". If this comment is based on a realistic understanding of the state of the art, then I have no argument, however my experience is that when drivers get behind the wheel of the cars and receive accurate information, they tend to be much more eager to take the leap.

So here is my hit list of reason's posed with the statement Maybe I'll Wait!

Cost

A very real concern for many people is that Electric Vehicles are expensive. Certainly this was true when the first vehicles entered the market, even with subsidies available in most countries, the price was high. If you were hoping for the savings in fuel costs, you would need to consider five or more years of savings just to equal the additional expenditure on the vehicle. At the time of publishing this book the costs have naturally dropped. With subsidies still in place in many regions, the cost has now reached a par with vehicles of the same class....but stop, this is not totally fair.... in my view the EV's are of far higher specification than the entry model I.C.E vehicles in the same class, so in reality, EV's offer greater value.

I haven't mentioned Tesla very often so far, however here is one area, where Tesla has been both a help, and a hindrance to the industry. On one hand Tesla has led by example and effectively forced the mainstream car companies to get serious about electric vehicles. On the other hand, their (well thought out) strategy of building high end, hand built vehicles while they were proving the technology, has left many consumers with the association that electric vehicles are expensive vehicles. While Tesla has made progress on the mass market Model 3, at the time of writing, they still haven't delivered serious production line vehicles. *(Beware, that the main stream guys don't catch up and secure the market.)*

Risk

There is always a risk involved in being an early adopter, however at this point in time, we are gone well past the early adopter stage. Starting with the earlier generation hybrid vehicles such as the Toyota Prius, the battery health and electric components have all been well tested. Furthermore, taking the example of battery chemistry, so much has been learned and improved during this time. It has greatly improved the experience in the EV world today.

It is also worth noting that the vehicle manufacturers

were originally a little cautious regarding the rate of fast charging in early models. This was a smart move, as they were ensuring that they were not leaving themselves exposed to warranty claims. However today the warranty T&C's are less restrictive, demonstrating a growing confidence in the technologies.

Finally on the topic of risk, as most brands are now offering electric vehicles as part of their range, more and more workshops are fully equipped and qualified to service the vehicles. More choice means better value and fewer restrictions when you are thinking about servicing your vehicle.

Variety

So now that I have mentioned the growing range of vehicles, it is probably a good time to elaborate on what that means for the market. Almost all mainstream brands are now offering full electric, plug-in hybrid electric or both across their range. Many have made bold promises stating that future models will no longer offer petrol and diesel engines. While I often say that "the devil is in the detail" regarding timings as well as the substantive meaning behind the claims, it is none the less significant in where the industry is moving.

From a driver's perspective, many are loyal to, or at least have a preference for a particular brand. I only need to look at friends, colleagues and neighbours to identify that many stick with the same brand when changing their car. Whatever the reason for this decision, whether it's trust in the dealership or the status associated with a particular brand, it is clearly important. This has had the effect of excluding many buyers from seriously considering an EV in past years, when the number or makes of electric vehicle was very limited.

At this point in time, almost all car companies are manufacturing and selling EV's, so if you think that your favourite brand isn't there yet, there is a strong possibility you are out of date.

Autonomy

The number of km/miles you can drive before refilling is regularly quoted as a reason to avoid EV's for the moment. In the early days of EV's this was genuinely an issue for many who would otherwise have liked the notion of going electric for their next car. Over the last few years this has become less of an issue, EV's are coming with more powerful batteries and greater autonomy.

The improvements in autonomy have brought some of the informed into the game. However as I get in or out of my EV, I am regularly asked about the driving range and I generally see the same astonished expressions when people hear what distances are really possible (and I quote real values, not brochure values). But this is not the only barrier.

I have been involved in a number of user experience groups related to electric vehicles. Most participants have been asked the question, how many kilometres they drive in a day, a week and a year. It is amazing how many intelligent, 'clued in' people over estimate the real distances covered. In fact, even after they have trialled an EV for a number of weeks/months, without restriction, when asked the same question again, most still over estimate.

Technology improvements

When most people go to buy a computer or a phone, they generally accept that there will be a new model out within a couple of months. The realisation exists, that this is life and that they cannot wait forever. Therefore, when purchasing, they rarely wait, but instead purchase the highest reasonable specification they can afford.

In the case of an EV many potential buyers want to wait until technologies improve. I recognise that the investment in a vehicle is far greater than most other devices and therefore influences the decision, however there are a couple of other things to remember.

At this relatively early stage in the uptake of EV's many countries still offer incentives. Whether these are tax breaks or free fuel, they all contribute to lowering the cost of ownership for the buyer. We should remember that, as the migration becomes more substantial, governments will start to reduce the incentives in order to revert to a sustainable economic environment. The moral of the story is "If you have answered the other questions to your satisfaction... Buy sooner rather than later".

Related to the same hesitation, is the question; whether the re-sale value of the vehicle will fall as newer technologies are introduced. In my view, this is not a significant risk. My reasoning is as follows: First of all current offerings of EV's are recognised to be highly subsidised by the manufacturer, this along with government subsidies has actually meant that the cost of todays vehicles is unnaturally low. As vehicle battery costs drop, vehicle manufacturers are likely to recoup their margins, meaning that the price tag on the vehicle will not drop. Furthermore in order to regain expected margins, as the vehicle battery size gets larger, the manufacturer is still likely to increase the price, even though the cost has reduced. On top of this, any government subsidies will fall off when the momentum of migration is self-sustaining. This will at least maintain the cost of new vehicles, which will in turn, maintain the cost of second hand vehicles.

During the early days of EV's, the lack of second hand vehicles was a barrier to entry for those who traditionally only buy pre owned vehicles. The size of this market is substantial and therefore this demand will ensure that fair market prices are achieved.

As drivers become accustomed to choosing and purchasing an EV, we can expect that not everyone will want the largest battery size. It's a lot like choosing between a 2-litre engine or a 1-litre engine, based on your driving profile. So panic not, that you will be left with a worthless vehicle.

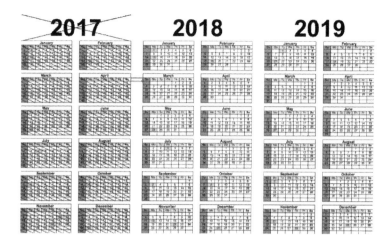

The real reasons to wait

I promised at the outset to be fair and balanced. So far in this chapter, I have been very much in the corner of EV's. Now it's time to balance the scales just a little.

I am not suggesting for one minute that Electric Vehicles are the one stop solution for all drivers. As of today......., not by a long shot. However I do believe that they would suit far more drivers than realise it.

When deciding whether or not to migrate to electric, you should first make sure your facts are up to date. The industry has changed much over the last few years and the next few years are likely to show similar evolution.

Be realistic with your driving needs. If you genuinely require long distance driving on a regular basis, then unless you are prepared to fork out a significant sum for a vehicle with a very large battery, EV's are not for you...yet. If on the other hand, you are mostly within the realistic range of an

50

electric vehicle that suits your budget, you can always look at renting a car or taking a train for that rare occasion you need a longer distance. Don't forget, fast charging is available, so if these longer trips are less frequent, then you might just decide to add a little extra time to your journey for a charge, a coffee and a bathroom break.

Currently most electric vehicles are 5 seater vehicles. This may be one of the strongest reasons for a parent who needs to ferry a few kids complete with bicycles or prams or recreational equipment to stay clear of EV's for a while. Just stay up to date with what vehicles are available.

Finally if you have considered each of the reasons mentioned above and armed with true and up to date information still believe that you should wait, then I have no further reason to try and convince you otherwise.

Chapter 6

Buying An Electric Vehicle

Many people who test-drive an electric vehicle want to buy one. If they have convinced themselves that an EV will work for them, then the driving experience will seal the deal. However, in order to ensure that a somewhat impulsive purchase is a good long-term decision, you should still decide based on some simple criteria that you might use to purchase any vehicle. I tend to ask people some basic questions as a way to determine if an EV is suitable and what type of EV would work for them.

Not every product "*Does exactly what it says on the tin*". Unfortunately the motor industry is often left wanting on this front. I should clarify however, that the failures I will mention are not down to any particular manufacturer telling lies, but rather all manufacturers being obliged to follow industry standard testing protocols that don't reflect reality. This means that when it comes to the driving range of the vehicles, they are all fairly equally detached from reality. Must of us know that the petrol vehicle we buy will not live up to the MPG or l/100km rating advertised in the brochure, however because distances are quite large and refuelling is still common place, we are not worried. In the case of EV's because vehicle autonomy is still growing and charging availability may not have reached every area, we are very sensitive to the percentage short fall. In Europe, the New European Drive Cycle (NEDC) is the standard test that vehicles must rate against. Drivers often refer this to as "*the down hill with the wind behind you test*".

When you are purchasing an EV, get some real advice and preferably take a vehicle for a long run, to get a feel for what it really does. In my experience, I have seen customers who were sold a vehicle based on the brochure specification, very disappointed, despite the fact that the vehicle is more than adequate for their day-to-day needs. On the other hand I have met many drivers who received realistic information that suggested that the vehicle was borderline for their requirements and they are very happy. In communications terms, they refer to this as expectation management.

All vehicles use more fuel for heating or cooling the cabin on extreme days than they do on moderate days. Therefore make sure that when you test drive or hear other drivers telling of their experience, that you allow for the span of weather conditions you would typically experience. In some older vehicles, this could affect the driving distance by up to 30% whereas most modern vehicles can be as low as 10%.

How far do you really drive on an average day?

Many drivers only travel small distances in a day. If you stop and think, many of you will admit to traveling far less than 80km (50 miles) in a day. If you work at a fixed location, it should be easy to calculate your round trip including any detours or stops along the way. These commutes are likely to account for much of your weekly driving. Equally, if you are the one who works at home and looks after the school runs for the kids, the calculation is similarly easy to work out.

Next comes the weekends or leisure days. These are often much harder to figure out. In my case, I can calculate my week quite easily, however my weekends vary dramatically. In the case of the weekends, I can look back over the previous year and put a fair estimate on my driving. If you can say that you generally stay within e.g. 40km (25 mile) radius of your home, or on the other hand, that every other weekend you travel to your family or in-laws 200km (125 miles) away, this can be invaluable when deciding whether or not, to go electric.

How often do you travel on longer journeys?

A regular rebuke of any suggestion that EV's are suitable for some people is that these people travel long distances. This is a very real consideration, but stop.... how often do you make these journeys and is there an alternative way to travel.

Lets be clear; if you need to travel long distances regularly, this is an important consideration, however if you really only make these longer journeys a hand full of times a year, it might be possible to arrange other methods to fulfil these needs or simply just stop and recharge and enjoy a short break along the way.

Is there a second car in the family?

This is very much tied to the previous question. If you have a second car in the family, then it is worthwhile considering whether you can swap vehicles once in a while to accommodate everyone's needs. Just be careful, the other driver may not want to give the EV back. In many cases an electric vehicle is purchased as a second car, however in reality, most owners use them more than the I.C.E equivalent.

What do you use the car for?

This is probably an understated question. If you need your car almost like a small minibus, then there is currently a limited number of vehicles available. However as the number and range of vehicles is growing, this last statement is likely to be out of date soon after publication. My point is, that if the EV's on offer don't match up to your needs regarding number of passengers or equipment being carried, then you may need to wait until your next purchase before migrating to electric.

Can you install a charge point at your home?

The possibility to have a charge point installed at home is frequently the dealmaker or breaker for prospective EV buyers. While not being able to install a charge point at home, doesn't completely exclude you from owning an EV, it definitely makes life a lot more complicated.

People who live in apartment blocks often experience difficulty in gaining permission for a charge point at their car park, regardless of whether spaces are assigned or communal. This issue is understandable, as management companies do not really want any extra work maintaining the equipment or administering payment for energy used. Furthermore while the building power supply may be adequate for a small number of vehicles, it might have difficulty coping with large quantities. As yet commercial solutions for apartment charging are limited, however this area is changing fast.

Whether you can install a charge point at home, or alternatively have access to charging near your home overnight, you will have peace of mind, that each day you will leave with a full battery and that you will have at least the driving range of a full battery, before you get home.

Have you access to convenient charging facilities away from home?

For much of the week many of us adhere to a very fixed schedule. So my next question is, whether you can acquire a charge at some regular point during that schedule. If we consider the time we spend in work, often 8 hours a day, it is an ideal opportunity to pick up a charge when you typically just park up the car and leave it until going home time. Employers are now considering and installing EV charging in car parks. In some cases, this is a way to wave a green flag and get some good press for being environmentally friendly, in others it stems from a genuine wish to facilitate staff to move to cleaner, cheaper fuels.

The bottom line is that if you can access charging during your working day, it will increase the usability of an EV for you. Moreover if this is combined with home charging, it would double the achievable commute possible for the EV.

The Final Decisions!

New or Second Hand?

Lets say that in general, you have decided that an EV is for you. What else do you need to decide? First is do I buy new or buy a pre-owned vehicle. This is far more of a lifestyle choice than anything else. Some people only ever buy new and some people are completely opposite, opting for a vehicle of a few years old every time. I won't get into the economics versus fashion or status. I will stick to some basic points. Firstly, at this point in time there is a growing and healthy level of second hand EV's on the market. Those early adopters are on their second or even third EV having traded in their old vehicle to a proud second hand buyer.

If you are going second hand, you need to be just as diligent as if you were buying any vehicle. In this case, check the service history and look for a battery health report. The battery health report is a good way to ensure that the vehicle will serve you well over the coming years.

Battery Size.

When you are looking around at vehicle options, you should be conscious of the battery size. However I would caution, that bigger is not always better. This really depends on your driving profile. For example, my profile would warrant a 40kWh battery, however my wife's profile sits well inside the comfort zone of a 24kWh battery. If you opt for a larger battery, you will part with more of your hard earned cash. But that's not all; you will also be carrying around a larger, heavier battery, which if you don't need it, is just affecting your efficiency when driving.

Optimise the battery selection to your real driving profile and consider substituting a heavier underutilised battery for a couple of short recharging stops a year.

Charging speed.

We will cover chargers in more detail in the chapter 'Refuelling your EV', however for now here are some important points when choosing an EV.

On board charger is the term given to the item in a vehicle that converts AC power to DC power suitable for recharging the battery. This is slightly different to a DC fast/rapid charger. So what should the buyer consider?

When choosing a vehicle, find out the size of the on board charger and find out if it is a single phase or a 3-phase charger. Some countries have 3-phase power available at domestic properties, others normally only install a single phase as standard. A vehicle which has a single phase charger can charge on a 3-phase supply and vice versa, however the transaction will be limited to the lowest rated device, either car or charge point. In the early days most EV's charged at 3.6kW (16Amps) and only on one phase. While some vehicles now come as standard 7.2kW (32Amp) single phase, on others this is an option. Three phase vehicles use the same rates but multiplied across 3-phases, hence they are rated as 11kW and 22kW.

When charging overnight, even the lower charge rate is fine unless, you are replenishing a very large battery. However during the day, when you are looking for a convenient top up, you may prefer a higher charge rate. For this reason paying a small premium for a larger on board charger is often worthwhile.

PHEV

The topic of hybrids versus full electric was covered in the chapter 'All Electric or Hybrid', however for the purpose of this chapter we will briefly mention the subject again. If you are faced with the choice of a Full Electric Vehicle or a Plug-in Hybrid Electric Vehicle, you are probably borderline for whether the technology is right for you yet. The easy option would be the Hybrid, however be sure that the realistic electric driving range of the vehicle is suitable to ensure you are in electric mode for most of your journey most days. If not, you will be paying a lot for petrol or diesel to carry around an electric motor and battery pack.

Battery Lease

When buying an electric vehicle you may be presented with the requirement or at least option to lease the battery. Most vehicle manufacturers today only offer the battery with the sale of the vehicle. A couple sell you the vehicle and require you to lease the battery. These same companies are migrating where you may have the option of buying or leasing the battery.

The explanations for the battery lease model can differ depending on your perspective. On one side, it is supposed to give the buyer a level of security regarding the risk of battery failure or even changing battery technology. On the other hand it helps to lower the up front cost of the vehicle, opting instead to pay over the ownership lifecycle of the vehicle.

Most car companies have a bank attached to the brand. I am sure that there are many intricacies of financing that allow the brand to save moneys, particularly where they may themselves, be leasing the battery from the battery manufacturer.

The big question regarding battery lease is whether or not you trust the battery technology. If you are like me and trust the technology, you probably won't want to lease a battery, after all, the cost equates to approximately a tank of petrol each month. As for the idea of accessing newer battery technology, this is, as far as I am concerned, very unlikely.

A fair question regarding battery lease is; how do I transfer the lease to another person when I sell the car and what if that person has a bad credit rating with the banks? Well so far this has not been an issue. The motor companies are ensuring that the transfer is kept fairly simple and that the new vehicle owner will have no issue obtaining a lease.

I have however witnessed two issues: The first is where a vehicle was being imported from another country. In this case, there was a long and drawn out process, with the new host country distributor not wanting to take on the battery lease agreement. The second issue presents itself when you look at second hand values of vehicles. In this case I have witnessed a number of vehicles offered for surprisingly low prices. I have enquired as to why, only to be told that the battery lease was putting a lot of people off purchasing.

Chapter 7

Servicing An EV

Not everyone considers the servicing of a vehicle when they first think about purchasing one. In the case of an electric vehicle there are reasons to consider future servicing requirements that may influence your purchase decision.

The Evolution of EV Maintenance

When EV's started to appear first, only a handful of technicians were qualified or experienced enough to carry out maintenance on them. Early EV's were often supplied as a retrofit of a combustion engine vehicle carried out by a third party company. This complicated matters more, because the traditional vehicle repair centres tended to know very little about the electric drive systems. The effect of this lack of knowledge was to drive up the cost of servicing, sometimes requiring a technician to travel long distances to investigate an issue or carry out repairs.

Today, qualified technicians can be found in most areas. As the number of vehicle manufacturers producing EV's increases, service shops are being equipped and technicians trained across the dealer networks. My experience of having my EV serviced is that it takes less time and costs less than my previous petrol or diesel vehicles.

What's in a Service?

The small number of moving parts in an EV as well as not having a large quantity of oil in an engine block immediately indicates that you should expect a reduction in the cost of a service. The reduced number of moving parts means less potential for parts wearing down. A small amount of coolant is still present as well as brake fluids, however these items tend to require less replacement or topping up than engine oils. Alternators, starter motors, spark plugs, fuel filters and a string of other items susceptible to wear are all missing from EV's.

Braking systems in an EV are more efficient than those of a combustion engine vehicle. Regenerative braking uses the motor to slow the vehicle down, while putting energy back into the battery. This minimizes the amount of friction braking required and therefore the amount of wear on the brake pads and disks. I have experienced vehicles with almost 100,000km still very comfortably using the original set of brakes.

A typical service will involve an inspection of all the main components as well as the safety equipment in the vehicle. It will also involve checking levels of coolant and brake fluids. A service should include running a diagnostic report, which will alert the service technician to any system alarms or faults. The diagnostics report will also typically give you an assessment of the state of health of the battery. As a vehicle owner, you should ensure that you get a copy of the battery health report, as it may be important for prospective buyers if you are selling the vehicle.

Parts List	Yes/No
Alternator	No
Fuel Filter	No
Engine Oil	No
Carburetor	No
Spark Plugs	No
Radiator	No

I have heard reports of reduced tyre wear on electric vehicles. This is credited to the 'eco' driving function, which softens the acceleration curve as the vehicle is pulling away from a stop. I can understand the logic, as it reduces the heating and friction on the tyre. I cannot claim to have any really hard data on this phenomenon, however I can tell you that I have driven over 60,000km on a set of EV tyres. When

I did go to change the tyres, I was able to find a suitable low energy match at a price comparable to what I would expect to pay for tyres on my previous vehicles.

Other than inspections and diagnostics, a typical service may replace, no more than the wiper blades and some window washing fluid.

Electric Motors

Electric motors are everywhere; they are all around the home, from the vacuum cleaner to the fruit juicer. Our experience of them is generally speaking very positive. Where an appliance with a motor does go faulty, the problem rarely turns out to be the motor.

I have spent many years working in industry and much of this time involved maintenance of plant and equipment. I have direct experience of motors running 24/7 continuously for months at a time, without any sign of strain. The technology is well proven.

Some have argued that EV motors are more compact and therefore could give rise to overheating problems. Another suggested source of problems may come from the vibration and shock coming up from the road as we drive. So far, I have seen no evidence that these are significant sources of failures. Automotive engineers have addressed far greater challenges and I am confident that they have taken actions to mitigate against these issues also.

The Battery

The big-ticket item in an EV is the battery. While battery prices have fallen considerably over the last few years and continue to fall, they are still the major component in the cost of an EV.

So far, the number of battery faults I have read about, has been small. Moreover a battery pack is made up of individual cells, which are grouped into modules. In the case of a battery fault, the remedy is likely to be an individual or small number of modules rather than the complete battery pack.

When the battery pack finally reaches the point where it is no longer holding enough charge, the solution is likely to be found by replacing a small number of modules, which will prolong the life of the vehicle. I discuss batteries in a little more depth in the chapter "So, What About The Battery". In this I elaborate on the options for prolonging the life of the vehicle when battery health starts to effect performance.

Chapter 8

Sustainability & The Environment

Depending on your perspective this chapter could take one of two directions. In the interest of being balanced I will attempt to address the key issues on both sides of the debate. I should also nail my colours to the mast, when it comes to climate change. *I am not <u>totally</u> convinced that everything we are experiencing in the way of weather related events is as a result of mans effect on the climate. I believe that we <u>may</u> be experiencing some part of a natural cycle, which is not obvious from the limitations of historical records. <u>However</u>, I also believe that man is depleting resources and damaging the environment, both to our detriment and the detriment of future generations. Whether climate change is caused by man or not, we should not continue to act blindly, with no regard to the impact we are having on our planet.*

Zero Emissions

I guess it was the marketing people who came up with the term '*Zero Emissions*', it's short it's snappy, but it may not be the most technically accurate. When people argue against electric vehicles, this term is quickly thrown back at the pro EV side. A more accurate term is zero tailpipe emissions, this reflects the fact that there is no combustion engine in the vehicle. After all, we all understand that the energy that powers the electric vehicle comes from the electricity system. Over the years our electricity system has become much cleaner, our reliance on fossil fuels has given way to cleaner sources of energy such as solar and wind generation. Countries who still burn large amounts of coal, one of the most polluting fuels, still produce electricity at an emissions level cleaner than those of combustion engine vehicles. Furthermore as our energy system cleans up, the story gets even better for electric vehicles. In fact electric vehicles themselves hold huge potential to assist in cleaning up the electricity system. With large amounts of energy storage available in electric vehicles there is an opportunity to use these batteries as a tool to balance the sometimes-intermittent generation from renewable sources.

This book is too short to go into a detailed analysis of '*well to wheel*' emissions. This topic has been covered by many scientific papers. In short when you consider the full environmental impact, fuelling an electric vehicle is still significantly less damaging than fuelling a combustion engine vehicle. For more information about how the electricity industry is fuelled, go to the chapter "Electricity & Zero Emissions".

Building the Vehicle

Building any product involves a carbon footprint. Electric vehicles are no different. The carbon footprint of an electric vehicle should in many respects be smaller than that of a combustion engine vehicle. The one major component of an electric vehicle, which comes into question, is the battery.

Any product, particularly a new product that is being built on a small scale, will inevitably produce a larger carbon footprint per unit than a mass produced product. The evolutional of electric vehicles is no different to that of the combustion engine, both started off small and grew over time.

When we remove the battery (which we will talk about next), the sum of all other components and the energy used to manufacture and assemble them is without doubt, massively less than that of a combustion engine vehicle of similar size.

Lithium and the Battery

Whether we speak of lithium, cobalt or any of the other mined minerals, which make up a battery, by weight alone the battery constitutes a large portion of the vehicle build. We must also consider the mining of materials and the practicality of recycling them.

All the key minerals are available in large quantities across the globe. In truth, the biggest issue is that some of them are clustered into geographical zones, which means that political and economic control could potentially influence availability (no different to oil, I hear you say). Some of the efforts to drive innovation in battery technology, stems from a desire to remove any dependence on particular countries or continents.

As abundant as the required minerals may be, just like oil, the supply is finite. However, unlike used fuel oil, we can recycle it. I have reviewed many documents on batteries, all of which point to the high recyclability of the components. Moreover, the battery cells can be used in second life applications after their first life as a vehicle battery has finished. After all, they are still recognized as having plenty of energy storage capacity, even if not practical for propelling a large vehicle.

A further point worth considering is that the vehicle manufacturers are responsible for the recycling of the battery. They have a large financial incentive to ensure that the battery is reused as much as possible before even considering recycling. The story of recycling is not all about cost, it is largely about opportunity. Battery technology has traditionally been very expensive, however the developments in electric vehicles and the potential for sourcing cheaper batteries through second generation sources will mean that batteries can be expected to reach far more products than ever before.

Distributed Generation

Generation of electricity at our homes or businesses is becoming a much more attractive proposition. As we generate the electricity, the greatest gain is generally only achieved when we use the energy ourselves, however, our demand profile doesn't always match our generation profile. In this respect, EV's can be of benefit. Vehicles parked at the premises during the time of energy generation can take the energy and store it for a later time, allowing the vehicle to be driven. The draw back here is that a smart system will need to be installed to control the charge pattern of the vehicle; otherwise you may spend too much effort connecting and disconnecting the vehicle. This smart technology is being developed and I have worked with some of it myself. In the not too distant future it is likely to be a common feature in the equipment we install.

Wind Farms and Solar Farms

The number of large-scale wind and solar generation projects around the world is growing rapidly. Many countries have set ambitious targets, with some promising to convert to 100% renewable by mid century. Depending on your geographic region there is likely to be wind turbines in your area or solar farms or both.

One of the drawbacks of this type of generation (particularly wind), is that the generation profile is uncertain. Forecasts are generated for these plants, however the level of error in forecasting means that sometimes the generation is significantly different to the prediction.

Balancing this is very important. Electricity systems need to be controlled to ensure system frequencies and voltages are maintained at the correct level to guarantee customer agreements. If these are not maintained, our machines will not operate correctly and this includes the other electricity generators such as Gas Turbines.

In this instance EV's can play a very significant part. The technology exists, to allow the control of electric vehicle charging in line with external commands. As yet however, the marketplace for these services is undeveloped. When energy regulators around the world provide frameworks within which a market can operate, I believe the service providers will play. Once this happens, there will be an incentive to use the electric vehicles to consume surplus power when available and stop consuming power when generation drops off. The end effect is that the energy system can allow greater amounts of renewable energy generation, while still maintaining grid stability.

Chapter 9

Refuelling Your EV

One of the sales pitches for an EV is that you never have to go to a filling station again or that you have a filling station right at home. Despite a large amount of truth behind this pitch, it is still very important to understand the various refuelling options, because for most people, they will at least occasionally still need to recharge away from home. It is also good to understand the limitations of charging at home.

Charging at home

The convenience of charging at home should not be underestimated. As a matter of simple routine, you arrive home and plug in your car, safe in the knowledge it will be full in the morning when you need to use it. Many vehicles even include timers or smartphone Apps that allow scheduling of charging to avail of cheaper night-rate electricity. These features also allow setting the climate control, to preheat the vehicle just before you leave the house. The advantage of the preheat feature is that you can do this while still connected to the household supply, reducing the effect of heating on the vehicles autonomy.

At the bottom end of the scale for charging a vehicle at home, some vehicles come with a cable known as a 'granny cable'. The term refers to the cable you use when you are at granny's house (and don't have a standard charger). This type of cable plugs into a standard domestic socket at your house. It is generally rated to allow a maximum current of 8-10 Amps. The reason for this is to avoid overheating the domestic circuit, which really is not rated for delivering its maximum power for hours at a time.

Domestic charge points come in a number of power sizes. For a house with single-phase electricity, chargers typically come as 3.6kW (16 Amp) or 7.2kW (32 Amp). For a house with 3-phase power, you can either install one of the single-phase units, or a 3-phase 11kW charger. It is very rare that a domestic dwelling would have a large enough power supply to accommodate a 22kW charger and even less likely that you could ever connect a 50kW DC fast charger.

In most regions, home chargers are only installed at 3.6kW. This is because the household supply may also have to feed energy to other large consumers such as storage heating or an electric shower. In some cases a 7.2kW charger can be installed, where the electrician is satisfied it won't overload the household supply. If you do manage to blow the fuse or circuit breaker in the house, it could take some time and expense to rectify the fault. Recently, some charge point manufacturers have started to offer a charge point that can monitor the household consumption, controlling the vehicle charge to avoid overload. This gives maximum benefit to the driver with reduced risk of overload.

If you are installing a charging point and intend to charge at home most of the time, then it will be much cheaper to be on 'night-rate' electricity. For this you will need a night meter or smart meter from your electricity network operator. These generally incur a standing charge each month, however it will be worth it, to be able to access cheaper electricity.

Always use a qualified electrician to install EV charge points.

Public Charging - On-Street.

On-street charging or charging in public parking is generally equipped with 22kW chargers, although some regions and operators have chosen to stick with 7kW or 11kW. While 22kW sounds wonderful, you need to consider the maximum power that the vehicle can accept. In many cases, vehicles can only accept a single-phase charge limited to approximately 7kW. This means that the charger will only deliver 7kW to the vehicle even though it is capable of supplying 22kW. At the end of this chapter, is a table that presents an estimate of how long it takes to recharge a vehicle at various rates of charge. Not everyone needs a full charge when they plug in, so public charging can be very convenient for a top up when you are at a meeting, going for lunch or shopping in the city.

Destination charging

The term destination charging refers to a location that is not your home base but also is not located on the street side. Typically the destination will not be a single residence, but rather a larger building such as a hotel or your workplace. For this reason, the charge points installed at these locations tend to fall into a category similar to the public charge points above.

Fast/Rapid charging

There is always lots of focus on fast charging, after all, we are all in so much of a hurry. Depending on where you live, there are two terms that overlap. The terms Rapid and Fast are both used to describe 50kW DC (or 43kW AC) charging. These charge points require a large power supply, much larger than is available at the typical home or even small business building. Fast charging is normally found in fuel station forecourts and supermarket car parks, any location where the driver might expect to be parked for 20-30 minutes.

There are two specifications for ~50kW DC charging and one specification for ~43kW AC charging. Vehicles with fast charging are only supplied with one of these specifications. As the industry was evolving there was also a bit of a power play between the DC technologies, for those of a certain age group, it was similar to the video tape battle between VHS and Betamax, (let's not get into the argument as to which was better :)

AC Fast Charging (~43kW) is utilised in a small number of vehicles. As of recently one of the original manufacturers to equip their vehicles with this standard has made the announcement that they will migrate to DC fast charging.

DC Fast Charging CHAdeMO (~50kW) was the original of the DC charging protocols. This specification came from the Japanese car industry. A useless piece of trivia is that CHAdeMO is supposed to be a pun for lets have a Cup of Tea, which represents the time it takes to charge.

DC Fast Charging CCS (~50kW) is a standard which came from the German car manufacturing industry. The acronym stands for Combined Charging System. This specification is making head way in Europe and seems set to become the European industry standard. A number of vehicle brands have announced plans to migrate to CCS from their original fast charging format. Furthermore, CCS has adopted a next generation, which will increase the limits of charging.

Tesla Supercharging (120kW) is the specification used by Tesla vehicles. The charge level far surpassed the original fast charge levels, hence the term 'Super Charger' however next generation charging is already being delivered to match and exceed this power level.

Next generation charging looks set to be based on CCS. This will allow charging up to **350kW** using the CCS connector. Currently plans are underway to install clusters of these chargers at motorway service stations across Europe. To put this in perspective, a vehicle with a real driving range of 450km would be charged in approximately twelve minutes.

The Connector

The connector type for on street AC charging is now standardized across most of Europe. These 'Type 2' connectors have seven pins, although depending on the vehicle and the charge point, two of the pins may not be utilised. Home chargers can be supplied with a tethered cable or a socket. If the socket is provided, it should be a 'Type 2' the same as the public AC chargers.

When it comes to DC charging, vehicle manufacturers are opting for either CHAdeMO or CCS. When looking at charging availability prior to a long journey, the driver will need to check that the charge points along the route have the required connector. Many of the chargers installed have both connectors attached.

Fast charge machines have the cable attached, you just need to take it from its holder and plug it into the vehicle. Standard chargers generally do not have a cable attached, therefore the driver needs to carry a cable in vehicle.

As electric vehicles were evolving, the AC connector was the subject of much debate. In some regions, the original connectors used were Schuko connectors similar to those installed in central European homes and offices. In France, there was a preference for the Schneider connector also known as the 'Type 3'. Thankfully this confusion has started to clear and current technology is converging on a single 'Type 2' connector.

Good Practice

As mentioned in the chapter "What About The Battery", the way you treat the battery will impact on its life expectancy. For this reason, it is good practice to consider battery charge levels and speed when charging.

While there are guidelines for good practice, I would consider them as just that; guidelines. They are not absolutes. If your vehicle warranty states absolutes, then you need to adhere to them, otherwise just be reasonable.

Most battery experts suggest that the optimum regime is to keep your battery between 20% and 80% State of Charge (SoC). This keeps the charge-discharge cycle in a range that the battery is comfortable with. However there is a second consideration. Some vehicle manufacturers have already taken this into consideration when designing the electric vehicle. I have monitored the energy transfer on a large number of vehicles. While some manufacturers state a battery size of 24kWh, the actual amount of energy that can be transferred is only 22kWh. This means that there is a portion of battery not within the reach of the driver and therefore helping to maintain the 20/80 rule. Other manufacturers are advertising the accessible battery capacity while a small additional portion is still available behind the software curtain; this also assists in maintaining the rule. I have however discovered one model of vehicle where the amount of transferable energy is greater than the advertised vehicle battery size. If you can see an energy meter on the charge points you are using, then get to know your vehicle.

Power	Charging Type	Voltage	Current Rating	Charging Times for 100km Electric Driving
3.6kW	SinglePhase AC	230V	16 Amps	6-8 hours
7.2kW	SinglePhase AC	230V	32 Amps	3-4 hours
11kW	ThreePhase AC	400V	16 Amps	2-3 hours
22kW	ThreePhase AC	400V	32 Amps	1-2 hours
43kW	ThreePhase AC	400V	63 Amps	20-30 minutes
50kW	DC	~400V (DC)	~125 Amps	20-30 minutes
120kW	DC	~400V (DC)	~350 Amps	10-12 minutes
350kW	DC	~800V (DC)	~430 Amps	2-4 minutes

Chapter 10

EV's In Fleets

For companies and organization considering Electric Vehicles as part of a fleet, it will be necessary to consider many of the topics similar to a private user. Don't however expect to come up with the same conclusions.

Rule Number One for most fleets is that the vehicle must complete its duty or else the business hurts. For this reason, the person responsible for the decision to purchase must be sure that the vehicle being considered is suitable to carry out the duties of the vehicle it is replacing. Where a private owner may be happy to accept a couple of small inconveniences regarding the charging, a commercial customer generally won't have that luxury.

Vehicle Size

The vehicle size is generally a good starting place. At present there are a limited number of commercial vehicles available and the larger you require, the smaller the choice. As with all areas of the industry, this is changing and more and more vehicles are coming on line. There are currently vehicles that can accommodate 1 and 2 Euro-pallets and there are up to 10 tonne vehicles available also. Heavy loads will impact the driving range, so get real life data or better still, try the vehicle yourself.

Peripheral Equipment

Does your vehicle require refrigeration or other peripheral equipment? If so, this may impact the driving range of the vehicle. Examine all the options including dedicated power supplies for the accessory equipment. There are many novel solutions to real life problems, so look around at what your industry is doing here.

The Driver

I have studied many potential fleet applications for Electric Vehicles. Some stack up and some don't. In a couple of cases, the physical vehicle is not an issue, however when you introduce a driver, it has potential to topple the argument. Here is an example. A delivery driver takes an electric vehicle in summer time, completes the route of approximately 100km and arrives back at base with 15% battery level in the vehicle. The driver loves the EV, because it is very smooth and comfortable to drive. The driver however moves on to another job and someone else takes up the route. Its now November and the weather is getting colder. The new driver however still wears shorts and a t-shirt and has the heating set to 30 Degrees C and leaves the vehicle door open while waiting for a signature from each customer. After completing 90% of the route, the battery is nearing empty and the vehicle needs a charge before returning to the depot. You can see where this is going.

Something as simple as changing a driver can be the make or break of EV's as a solution for a given fleet. In cases where the driver is always assigned to one vehicle, this can be addressed relatively easily, however where drivers float between different vehicles each day, there can be a lack of ownership that is more difficult to solve.

Distance Requirements

Obviously the distance that the vehicle can travel before recharging is a significant consideration. It doesn't need to have the biggest battery, so long as it has enough to carry out the work at hand, regardless of the time of year. Again, I cannot stress enough, the need to gather real life figures, as the brochures are not a representation of real life. Another very important factor is what you really know about the distances driven by the outgoing vehicle. If you use a vehicle tracker system, you should have a true reflection of needs, however it amazes me how many drivers and even fleet managers, don't have a true understanding of the vehicle needs.

Time to Recharge

When examining fleet vehicles, I have come across a number of cases, where some days a vehicle exceeds the distance that can be achieved by a particular EV. In these cases, the decision has hinged on whether the vehicle can access charging at an opportune time during the day. This could be during a lunch break or while the driver is carrying out other duties at the depot. This is often a case, where vehicles are operational across shifts and may have more than one driver.

In this case, it will also be important to know, the speed of charge, in order to determine if sufficient time is available. Some vehicles have very slow charge rates and others can accommodate fast charging.

Charging Options

Choosing the method of charging is important. The first point, I'd like to stress, is that you may not need high powered fast charging and if you don't need it, there are a range of reasons why, you shouldn't install it. There are two easily defined occasions to charge. Over night charging is generally straight forward and a 7kW charger will often provide more than enough energy to the vehicle before it is needed in the morning. Opportunity charging is when you need to catch a short charge during the working day. Lets take the example of a lunch break; in this case the driver may have 30 minutes up to an hour, during which time a charge can be accessed. Using a 7kW charger, the vehicle can may add anywhere between 20 and 50km of driving to the day. If a vehicle can accept 22kW this could be up to 140km. DC charging at 50kW could add over 100km in a 30 minute break, however, slower charge rates are better for the vehicle battery and the equipment costs less.

Maintenance Costs

Often the advertising around electric vehicles emphasises the small number of moving parts compared to an Internal Combustion Engine. This is quite true and does impact positively on the maintenance requirements of electric vehicles. However there is even more good news. While a small amount of brake fluid is still present, engine oils are non-existent in an EV. Moreover brake pads tend to last far longer in an EV than a combustion engine vehicle. This is due to the regeneration systems of the vehicle, using the motor to slow the vehicle down long before friction braking is required. The end result is that I have seen EV brake pads, which were barely worn in, after almost 100,000km.

Apart from routine wear & tear considerations as above, it is worth considering the two obvious components. The battery and the motor. In the case of the battery, I will direct you to the chapter 'So What About The Battery' for more information; however, battery life expectancy is above the amount of time that most vehicles remain in a commercial fleet. After this time the cost of reconditioning a battery or repairing it, is expected to be reasonable. The motors look even more favourable. Having come from an industry where motors can run 24/7 for weeks and months at a time, I have confidence in the life expectancy of electric motors. I am aware of some additional considerations in an electric vehicle environment such as impact shock and cooling. In these cases, I have also experienced motors installed in similarly harsh environments, where the motors survive just fine.

Fuel Costs

The cost of fuel is one of the top agenda items for every fleet manager. As oil prices fluctuate this issue gains more and more focus. In the case of the electric vehicle the cost of fuel you can expect, should be considerably less than the diesel equivalent.

First lets consider the time of day that you are charging. Most regions have at least a day-time and a night-time electricity rate, some have more granularity through the day. This gives an opportunity for recharging a vehicle when energy costs are low. Moreover, many commercial premises pay quite small amounts for electricity consumption, sometimes as low as 50% of what a residential customer may be paying. When a fleet manager is considering fuel costs, there are a number of elements required to complete the cost calculation. First, what time of day will you charge. Second, what rate are you paying per kWh of electricity. Third, how far will each kWh take the vehicle. As an example, my EV uses ~16.5 kWh per 100km. I can charge at night and I pay €0.11 per kWh on night-rate electricity. Therefore, I pay circa €1.82 per 100km (I used to pay circa €10 per 100km in my previous Diesel vehicle). This equates to an 80% saving.

Chapter 11

Staff Parking & Charging

As electric vehicles are becoming more and more popular, there are few organizations that have not yet been asked about installing EV charging equipment in staff parking facilities. As the industry is evolving, the specific solution will differ from scenario to scenario and from region to region. Some employers who have installed charge points already, have taken the view that the amount of energy consumed is small and therefore that they do not wish to place a fee on the use of the chargers. In the early days, this may add up, the company may gain good will, both from the driver and the greater community, if may even had received some good publicity in industry or community publications. However, I would caution any company installing charge points for staff, that they need to consider the future. In a very short time, the demand is likely to increase significantly. The effect of this increased demand may have a couple of implications. Energy costs are likely to grow to a significant level, infrastructure costs will increase and the taxman may become interested in the Benefit-in-Kind, gained by the employee. In the case of the taxman, the organization is likely to have a duty to report such usage.

Don't panic just yet, there are solutions to most, probably all of the obstacles, you may encounter. *As you read down through this chapter, don't forget to read the chapter 'The Business Of Electric Mobility' as it will provide some additional information that you may find useful.*

Whatever part of the world you are located, there are some principles you will need to keep in mind.

Driver Expectations

It is important to understand what a realistic expectation of charging facilities might be for drivers. Should drivers expect to receive this benefit free of charge or would they be willing to pay a reasonable amount for the facility? Should the driver expect to be able to charge a 100kWh battery every day at the workplace or would they be happy to gain a charge that would allow them to commute to work.

Organisations thinking of providing charging facilities will need to answer these questions. Most organisations, I have worked with have come to the conclusion that providing a facility where an employee can gain enough of charge at a fair cost, to complete their commute is a reasonable position to take.

Power Ratings

The topic of power rating is one that crosses my desk almost every day. There is a common starting position that 'bigger is better'; therefore a 22kW charger should be installed. This is often not the wise thing to do. Installing large quantities of high power chargers can cause difficulties and increased cost for the host, and these expenses, may need to be passed through to the driver.

To find a solution, lets go back to the expectations of drivers. A reasonable expectation may be that the vehicle could receive enough charge to drive 100km before they are ready to go home after their shift. Even with a 7kW charge point and similar on-board charger in the vehicle, you should expect to be able to deliver 100km of driving range in between 2 and 3 hours.

On a final note regarding charger power rating, I am often asked if a particular power rated charge point can charge all vehicles. My answer is fairly universal: *Because all vehicles within a region adhere to the applicable standards, all vehicles are capable of charging at any charge point. However the lowest common denominator between the vehicle, the connecting cable and the charge point will determine the maximum power that can be delivered.*

Working Hours

The duration of the employee shift links to the previous two points. A nominal working day may be 8 hours, however in reality this could be just a couple of hours or it might be a 12 hour shift. This may impact on the amount of charge a driver can obtain while at work. I say may, because it might just as well be limited by the size of the battery in the vehicle. Before leaving this point, it is worth calculating one scenario: A vehicle with a large enough battery, charging at work for 8 hours at 7kW, would be able to accept 56kWh of charge. This would allow a driving distance of approximately 340km (212 miles).

Cost Recovery and Revenue

Once numbers of users have increased and increased energy consumption is noticed on the company accounts, it will soon be time to consider recovering this cost from the users. In fact, I would suggest that this stage in the evolution should be considered right from the start, even if you don't intend implementing cost recovery immediately. Various payment solutions are available in the marketplace. Most charge point manufacturers will have paired up with at least one of the service providers. I have seen coin machines and token machines, I have seen credit card solutions and online solutions, there are even premium rate SMS solutions on the market. One thing to be aware of, is that the market is still evolving and solutions will become more widespread and more functional. As with any technology, the race to provide the market winning solution will be a vicious battle and not everyone will survive. Therefore, I caution you to seek equipment based on industry protocols such as Open Charge Point Protocol (OCPP) managed by the Open Charge Alliance, rather than getting tied to a proprietary system, which locks you into one vendor for eternity.

Depending on the payment system chosen, you should be able to control the cost of the service, this may be based, on a subscription charge, energy consumption, duration or just a flat charge per charge event. As the host, you should be able to control the structure and return on these metrics. An example could be that you charge a small transaction fee along with the energy cost, to cover the cost of O&M as well as the energy consumption.

Third Party companies may be able to install infrastructure on your site and manage the complete system externally. This is a great way to limit the cost and administration associated with the service, however be careful not to hand over too much control to an organisation that may wish to operate beyond your comfort zone. While the service would not technically be your responsibility, your organisation could be deemed guilty by association.

Reporting

Whether for taxation reasons or environmental reasons, reporting is an important consideration when choosing both the charge point and the Charge Point Management System (CPMS). The charge point must have a means of communicating the data and the CPMS must compile the report.

Reporting for taxation is necessary in some regions, however many others have not yet focused on charging at the workplace as a potential revenue stream. The tax-man is really only likely to take an interest where charging is provided free of charge. In the case you are passing through the costs to the driver, then there is not likely to be any perception of Benefit-in-Kind.

Many organisations place a strong importance on gathering and reporting environmental and social impact across their sites. Therefore electric vehicles as a means of reducing the carbon footprint of employees commutes is often deemed a valid metric. I would go so far as to suggest that by installing EV charging at the workplace, you are not just reducing the carbon contribution of the commute, but also enabling a greater reduction through the non-work related mileage. The decision to purchase an EV is often weighted on the viability of the vehicle for the work commute, therefore having charging facilities at work may be responsible for enabling a wider carbon reduction.

Electricity Distribution

When installing charge points at the work place you will need to identify where the connection point will be for the charger. Ensuring that the distribution board is suitable and has sufficient spare capacity is very important. Moreover you should look to the future, giving consideration to what expansion is likely. Some distribution boards may only have a single-phase supply, where others have a 3-phase connection. This can determine whether you are limited to a particular charger power rating e.g. 7kW.

This is a good time to remind you that even if you have a 3-phase supply available; you should consider that you could install three 7kW chargers for every 22kW (3-phase) charger. When you are looking to increase the number of chargers, this can impact on the possibilities.

Maximum Import Capacity (MIC)

Closely tied with the topic of distribution is the MIC of the electricity supply. This is the limit of the amount of energy you can consume at a given time. If you exceed this amount, there are a couple of possible impacts. Firstly, and only partly connected, is that the main circuit interrupter for the building may disconnect you from your supply. This can be costly and time consuming to rectify. Secondly, your energy costs may increase disproportionately or you are served with a penalty for breeching your contract.

The moral of the story is, that you need to consider if large amounts of peak load, even if only for a short period are going to cause you to exceed your MIC.

Energy Management

Whether you are worried about the impact of large numbers of EV's on your network or just looking to optimise energy consumption with renewable energy generation on site, energy management should be of interest. In honesty however the solutions available, while interesting, tend not to be as functional as they should be. I believe the reason for this is that the market for energy services is still only developing and that some standards are missing to ensure flexibility. For this reason, many products offer a limited function that focuses mainly on the immediate distribution board and is generally based on a proprietary system. This means that only charge points of that manufacturer can operate with the energy management software.

In the coming years we can expect a number of more substantial offerings which will allow connection, both on a local level and externally. These offerings will need to be based on an industry protocol rather than proprietary in order to be as universal as consumers will demand. Protocols such as OCPP have evolved to take these future requirements into consideration.

Maintenance

Safety should always be a consideration whether at home or in industry. Any organization or business providing any service to its staff or customers has a duty of care towards those customers. In general, a good quality charge point will need very little maintenance, however I strongly suggest that it is at least inspected physically and electrically at a suitable interval. Water or dust ingress can cause malfunction or electrical insulation breakdown. Furthermore, circuit breakers and earth leakage detection should be tested. Regulation and requirements for electrical testing and inspection can be sourced at your regional electrical safety authority.

If you are contracting with an external company make sure that there is a maintenance regime in place that can support both safe operation of the equipment and quality of service indicators such as response to faults.

Chapter 12

Property Development & The EVSE

EVSE- Electric Vehicle Supply Equipment

Over the last couple of years, I have reviewed tender specifications for many property development projects. The quality of the specification have ranged from fair to dismal. The downfall of many specifications is the lack of practical knowledge of the engineer responsible, combined with a belief that everything you find on a search engine such as Google is accurate. Most of the specifications that have landed on my desk have been at least out dated, if not wholly unsuitable for the project they were intended.

For this reason, I have developed a training module intended to assist the engineering community to get up to speed and to be able to specify electric vehicle charging with a similar level of quality, comparable to how they specify fire detection, air handling and a myriad of other elements to a new or retrofit build. For details on how to organise a course, please contact training@eninserv.com

There are a number of questions which, when answered will guide the engineer towards a high quality specification.

How many users are expected? - this question will feed information towards how many charge points are required along with orders of magnitude of energy consumption.

Will the users be known? - explains the relationship between the user and the charge point host. It helps define methods of control and cost recovery. Systems installed for staff parking are likely to be very different to those required for a retail outlet.

Who are the tenants of the building? - guides us to find out whether it's a single owner or tenant, or is it multiple tenants with a landlord or property agent. This may be crucial to ensure that metering of supply is correctly configured, particularly where shared parking is specified.

What is the relationship between the user and the tenant? - will help establish the level of service expected and the practicalities of specific methods of authorisation and cost recovery.

What connections are available? - is a very important consideration when deciding on the locations and suitability of parking and charging spaces. There may be a need to spread out charging spaces or it might be practical and indeed desirable to keep them all in a single section of the car park. Additionally it may determine if 3-phase devices are suitable if desired.

What power is available? - is a slightly different question to the previous one, because it will focus on the overall capacity of the building or distribution board. It will guide an engineer to making the best choice of charge point to allow for maximum numbers of outlets and possible later expansion.

Who pays for the energy? - needs to be asked to determine both the suitability of connection to a particular metered supply and/or how users will be identified, authorised and charged for the usage. In some cases, a tenant may wish to have EV charging available for company vehicles, this might require reporting but no payment. On the other hand the tenant may be providing the service to staff or customers, both of whom may be expected to contribute towards the costs of providing the service.

How long will the EV's be parked? - will assist in determining the optimum output power of the charger. A vehicle belonging to an employee that is parked for 8 hours a day will not require a very powerful charge. A customer of a retail or food outlet may wish for a higher powered charge point (assuming there vehicle can accept the higher power), in order to maximize the benefit received in a short duration visit e.g. 1 hour.

How many EV spaces will be installed? - will again feed information towards the maximum loads and the amount of energy consumed. In some cases, this is determined by local planning laws, which may specify a percentage of spaces, which should be equipped with EV charging infrastructure. The local authority in my area, currently requires 10% of spaces on new development projects to be equipped for electric vehicles.

How many car parking spaces in total? - will assess the likelihood of expansion and the possible magnitude of this expansion. A development with a car park of 1000 spaces may only be equipped today with 20 spaces, however in the near future the demand for charging will increase and the development will be under pressure to install many more spaces. During the initial project, it may not be wise to install charging on a large percentage of spaces, however suitably sized cable ducts and local distribution boards installed today could save much expense and headaches later. Particularly as the technology is showing a level of adoption that suggests future expansion is inevitable. Power management should be a consideration, however at this point in time solutions are limited. In the near future though, I expect this to change.

While looking at the project as a whole, it would be worthwhile to write a short use case document, which includes answers to the above questions. This will help put the project into perspective both for the engineer and possibly for the potential solution providers bidding for the work. Single use sites vary from each other and mixed-use sites can be even more complicated. Unfortunately in the real world, you can only rely on the vendor to paint you a picture that includes his or her products. As the engineer, you will need to ensure you are sufficiently up to speed to safeguard your client.

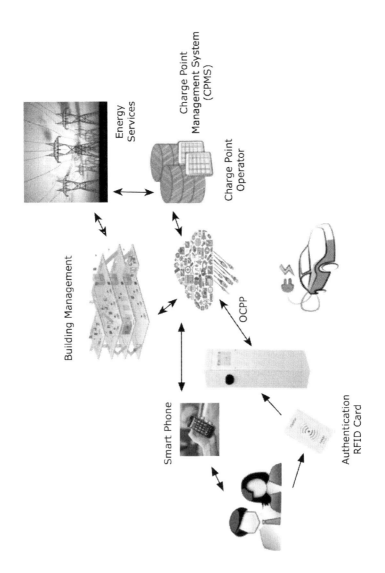

Energy Services

Charge Point Management System (CPMS)

Charge Point Operator

Building Management

OCPP

Smart Phone

Authentication RFID Card

When writing a specification you should be clear about the following items:

The number of charge points is a good starting point. When writing the document, be very clear about whether you are talking about charge poles or charge points. Often a charge pole incorporates two output sockets.

Whether the charging should be provided as single outlets or double outlet. Doubles tend to be a little cheaper than singles, assuming that the parking spaces are next to each other. You may wish to allow either singles or doubles depending on the cost.

Wall mounted or ground mounted. Wall mounted chargers are sometimes a little cheaper, however the more significant influence, may be the ability to eliminate the need for expensive ground works where wall mounted is practical.

The output rating of the socket should be clear. This should be determined by the user needs and the available connections. Remember, bigger is not always better.

State the required IP rating of the enclosures. This will be determined by the environment where the charger should be installed.

State the Socket or plug type. This will be partly determined by whether you require a lower power charger or a DC fast charger.

Communication requirements should specify how the charger will communicate with the outside world. Whether for payment purposed or simply reporting usage, this will be required.

Electrical protection requirements should be clearly stated. I recommend that each charge point outlet is equipped with individual circuit protection in order to best protect the users from faults.

IEC Specifications requirements will dictate the type of socket or plug in technical terms, however it will go further to specify the connection protocol and design safety standards. Some IEC standards will consider Vehicle to Grid (V2G) protocols, which may have an application. This is a good time to remind you, that some of the information online is out dated and not appropriate for today's installations.

Accessibility requirements are regularly omitted from specifications, however if you are designing a system for public use or employee use, you should ensure it adheres to suitable local standards for disability and mobility access such as ADA and DDA. The standards will most likely, be set by the same body responsible for requirements for locating light switches, keypad, display screen and other such equipment.

Status indication is important. Most charge points come equipped with very good status indication in the form of LED's or LCD display screens. There is generally no need for a fancy complicated display, however it is important that the basic status indications are available such as *Ready*, *Connected*, *Charging* and *Fault*. Some basic charge points have little or no indication.

Layout drawings are often omitted, however when

you are looking a number of vendors to bid for the works, layout drawings can be useful. Whether a vendor supplies single outlet machines or doubles or a choice, these drawings will often allow the vendor to offer a product best suited to needs.

Chapter 13

Electrical Installation

When it comes to electrical installation of an EVSE whether in a residential location or in a public or commercial location, many of the principles are the same. I do not intend to go into a lot of detail here, as it is a topic that I am not equipped to provide answers appropriate to each & all regions. I will however discuss some of the points, which are universally important.

I strongly recommend that only qualified electricians be used to install electrical fixtures including electric vehicle charge points.

It's Not Rocket Science

At the risk of sounding facetious, I deliberately used this heading because I regularly meet electricians who are afraid to touch a charge point due to not understanding what it does. From an installation perspective it is like many other appliances, which need to be installed according to local electrical safety regulations. So lets look at what you need to remember.

The charge point is an electrical appliance similar to many others, which is mounted on a wall or on the ground. The location for the charge point may be indoors or outdoors. Charge points may be single phase or 3-phase and their load may range from as low as 3.6kW up to 50kW and beyond.

IP Rating

The IP rating of an appliance or enclosure stipulates the level of protection from ingress of dust or moisture. This can range from no protection up to complete protection from ingress of each of these elements. As with any enclosure, the appropriate IP rating for a charge point will be determined by where the charge point is installed. Many charge points intended for outdoor use in a car park are supplied as IP55. This claims protection against solid bodies of greater than 1mm and protection against water spray from all directions. As a generality, this seems totally reasonable, however you will need to assess the environment where the charge point is to be installed.

Earthing

Many charge points are designed in an enclosure that is metallic or conductive. Even those that utilize a plastic or insulated enclosure however need to give consideration that the vehicles connected to them have conductive chassis' and that they are insulated from the ground by rubber wheels.

All EVSE's require an earth. When installing the charge point, the electrician will need to ensure that as well as connecting the circuit earth, a conductive enclosure is properly earthed as well as any doors on the enclosure. Likewise where Steel Wired Armour (S.W.A.) cable is used, the armour will also need to be appropriately tied to earth.

For some outdoor charge points, the earth impedance may require installation of an additional earth rod.

DC Fast Chargers

While I have stressed that in general, a charge point is just another appliance, I should also add a word of caution regarding larger 50kW chargers and particularly DC chargers. In this case, I would recommend that the Electrician seek specific installation information from the charge point manufacturer, either through the installation manual or by contacting them directly. The protection requirements for devices of this size and where DC current is delivered to the vehicle go beyond the scope of this guide.

Isolators

When installing a charge point, the electrical regulations in many regions require the installation on an isolator before the appliance. In this case, the electrician will need to adhere to the local rules, while being practical about the location and access to the isolator to avoid nuisance switching.

Load Protection

Circuit breakers to protect from load should be sized correctly for the charge point. When doing so, you will need to remember that if the charge point has more than one outlet, you can expect overall power rating is that of one socket multiplied by the number of sockets. e.g. 7kW x 2 = 14kW total, which implies a current of approximately 64 Amps could be drawn.

Having calculated the total current draw of the charger, you will then need to ensure that all cables and components down stream of the circuit breaker are protected. A charge point should ideally come equipped with an internal circuit breaker on each socket, this means that all the internal contactors and cables are sufficiently protected. For example, many charge points are equipped with a contactor and internal wiring suitable to supply up to 40 Amps to the vehicle, where the vehicle draws 32 Amps, installing a 63 Amp or 80 Amp breaker for a double socket will not protect the device sufficiently. For this reason, it is desirable to have outlet specific protection built into the charge point.

Earth Leakage Protection

Protection against electric shock is generally provided by an RCD or similar earth leakage protection device. Regulations in most regions require a 30mA device is installed on each power supply. Again, many of the better quality charge points come with a suitable device installed. If the charge point is not equipped with a suitable device, you will need to install one on the main feed out to the charge point. While some regulations specifically state that RCD's are not connected in series, I have seen cases, where a 100mA RCD has been installed ahead of a 30mA RCD. This seems to me to be a reasonable way to protect a person from electrical shock, while offering some level of discrimination in the circuit.

Testing

After any device is installed it should be tested. These tests should include a functional test, along with a series of appropriate electrical tests. Electrical tests should include an earth impedance test to assess the quality of the earth bond to the charge point. If the impedance is too high, the earth connection may need to be improved. This may require cleaning of contacts, a larger cross section earth wire or installation of an earth rod in the proximity of the charge point.

Insulation testing should also be carried out on the cable and main power circuit. This will determine if the insulation protection between conductors is appropriate.

Earth leakage devices should be tested to ensure that they function correctly. While the devices should have a test button, to check that they switch, this is not sufficient for an electrical installation. Current levels and trip times will need to be measured in accordance with electrical regulations and the device type.

For a full list of required tests and for appropriate test criteria, please consult your local regulations.

Chapter 14

Battery Swapping And Induction Charging

One of the most enjoyable elements of my work in the e-Mobility space has been working on and assessing many new developments as the technology has evolved. Most of these are driven by perceived user requirements, obstacles in the way of adoption and potential impacts of EV's on other parties, such as electrical network operators and the likes.

There are three sets of technology under the headings battery swapping and induction charging which I am regularly told are the holy grail of the EV industry. In reality there are pros and cons to each and often there is a disparity between the most effective technology and a sustainable business. Lets look at those technologies.

Battery Swap

Battery swapping is the big-ticket item. Well its already here and it has been here for a while. So let me nail my colours to the mast. The industry would benefit greatly, from a way to replenish batteries in a very short time. In recent times, the development in high performance charging is indicating that help is on the way. However battery swapping is here and I firmly believe that a mechanism that allows the driver to enter a refuelling station with a depleted battery and leave a few minutes later with a full battery is a fantastic feature for any driver. So yes, it is desirable. But unfortunately the story doesn't stop here:

Lets say, I buy a new car and drive around on my new battery. After a week of charging at home, I find myself availing of the very convenient service of a battery swap station. After just a couple of minutes, I drive out of the station with a full battery. After a couple of days, I notice that I am getting less range than I had experienced during the previous week. So I head for my car dealer and ask them to check. A short time later they tell me that the battery in the vehicle is 8 years old and operating at about 80% of what a new battery would deliver. Are you getting the picture?

Battery swapping can only really work if you are subscribing to a model where you lease the battery from your battery swap service provider.

So lets say, this sounds interesting and you subscribe. One week later you are away from your locality, when you stop by another battery swap station. Your service provider is not operating here, so this company tells you they cannot assist. However the helpful attendant does inform you that the company down the street has a roaming agreement with your service provider. Off you go, and happily swap your battery to allow you to complete your day.

Behind the scenes, batteries transfer in and out of multiple competing operators stations. As with any proactive company, your operator notices that the state of health of some of their batteries is deteriorating much faster than expected. Battery diagnostics suggest that the battery has been aggressively charged and the blame game starts between operators.

Next: Battery swapping requires cooperation between service operators and the vehicle manufacturers. This can all be easily achieved, however cooperation between competing vehicle brands regarding battery pack shape and size, is a much more difficult proposition. Therefore the battery swap service provider will need to stock multiple sizes of battery pack, for various vehicle brands and models. In the early days of EV's this is not such an arduous task, however roll on to the time when the majority of vehicles on the road are electric. We may have a bigger issue.

I have used battery-swapping stations and they are fantastic. Its just like one of the car wash machines that moves the car along the process until it arrives out the other side. I have also visited the warehouse at the rear of the station where all the batteries are stored and picking systems transfer the batteries from the charging bay, to the vehicle. While visiting a swapping station on one occasion, I was chatting with a colleague from one of the large German automotive companies, when a bombshell dropped. I turned to Holger and asked if he noticed anything about the warehouse. The thing that struck me was, how much space was required for a relatively small number of batteries. Even if we put our engineering hats on, to minimize the space, we could not be that much more efficient. The level of real estate required to operate a quality service at the stage of mass adoption of the technology would be colossal.

While I would be happy to see a practical and workable solution, I am also conscious of the developments in both battery size and speeds of charging. Both of these will dent any business model on which battery swapping could exist.

Static Induction Charging

Now this is a somewhat different and more likely development. First a summary definition: Static Induction Charging is where a vehicle comes to a stop with the vehicles induction coil positioned above the primary coil of a charging pad, after which time charging can commence. *(Just like a big version of your electric toothbrush.)*

I have been involved in the development and testing of one such device. The project focused mostly on the possible uses and gains of induction charging against the more common plug-in arrangement. Our goal was not the development of a product. The technology functioned very well. We assessed safety concerns, efficiencies and practicalities around induction charging and the results were very positive.

There is a small obstacle regarding standardization. Vehicle manufacturers would need to agree on and adopt a standard. This is all achievable, it has already been agreed on the majority of conductive systems. So where do we go from here?

A number of companies have developed inductive systems. To-date these are effective retrofit solutions. Some exploratory partnerships have been entered into, however we are yet to see a major car company make a big bold step. That time will probably come soon enough.

From assessing the possible routes to adoption, my guess, is that the technology may get its first grip on a market, through either luxury vehicles where the additional cost is not such an issue, or through the taxi and shuttle bus market where users may want to maximise charge during opportunity stops at frequently visited locations. The value proposition may stack up in both these scenarios.

After adoption in some early market sectors, it is possible that, as the technology gets cheaper to produce, it will filter its way down from the luxury vehicles through the food chain until if eventually becomes a feature in all offerings *(just like electric windows)*.

Dynamic Induction Charging

Another summary definition: Dynamic Induction Charging is where a section of roadway equipped with a series of primary coils from a charging system transfers a charge to the secondary coil mounted on vehicles which travel over the charging lane.

There have been a number of articles about roadways, which have been equipped with dynamic charging. Having had the pleasure of working with many first rate engineers, I have no real doubt about what is achievable with technology. Furthermore, when I consider the convenience of picking up a charge while on the move, the perpetual motion of the EV, so to speak, I really like the notion. I also have fewer concerns about safety than some critics, as I am confident in the ability to control the power to the primary coils to align with the presence of a vehicle overhead. At this point, if you are a pedestrian, the potential of an electrical hazard will be far less than that of the vehicle traveling at speed, if you get my picture.

As with any technology, I try to focus on the sustainability of a business rather than on the achievements of the electronics. I run workshops with a heading "Engineer meets Customer" *(or investor)*, aimed at closing the gap between the very best technical solution and what the customer really values. After all, the most innovative technology will still disappear into the vaults, unless investors invest and customers part with their hard earned cash.

Where does Dynamic Charging stand in terms of sustainability?

As mentioned earlier, the energy of vehicle batteries is increasing and the speed of charge is also growing to meet demand. This is likely to reduce the necessity for charging on the go, leaving the benefit in the realms of convenience.

Furthermore the cost of producing dynamic charging is substantial. It will include power distribution over large areas as well as all the control functions necessary for it to operate. On the other hand the number of customers utilising the charging infrastructure can be expected to be proportionally better than one charging station for one vehicle.

Next comes the energy consumption. In real life this cannot really be expected to be provided free of charge. Therefore, it will have to be metered. If the meter is installed on the roadside, it will have to incorporate a complex system of identifying and bill the user by a traceable method. An alternative would be to have a subscription model, where users pay for access, however this too comes with difficulties and potential for massive imbalance between the values gained from some users over others.

Installing metering in the vehicle is another possible solution, however this also comes with the difficulty of validating and calibrating energy metering systems. It also separates the electricity meter from the utility, which may or may not be an issue depending on who is operating the system.

All in all, I find it hard to see dynamic induction charging stacking up. While static charging will probably filter its way down to the average driver over the next 10-15 years.

Chapter 15

Energy Management

Energy management in all areas of electricity consumption has come under the microscope. Electric vehicle charging, particularly where multiple charge points exist together will also require solutions. By using the term solutions, you may be led to believe that there is a problem. Indeed while multiple charge points can cause problems for the buildings power supply, it can also present opportunity that can be maximized through the use of energy management products.

What is Energy Management?

Energy management is the optimisation of energy consumption. It assists in the reduction of absolute energy consumption or the reduction of energy costs.

So this is one of many definitions, but what does it mean in real terms. As we use electric vehicles and attempt to recharge them, we can be contributing to a problem for the electricity network or we can be contributing to a solution towards another issue that the network or grid is experiencing.

Many observers have sited the potential for the electricity system to become overloaded as vehicles arrive home after a day's activity. The theory goes, that all vehicles will be looking to charge at the same time around 18:00 or

19:00 hours each evening. This could cause significant strains on the electricity network.

Those active in the EV space also see opportunities related to the charging demand and specifically the battery associated with an EV. This scenario sees the EV being asked to accept a charge at times when renewable energy is in good supply and being asked to reduce charging rates when renewables are in shorter supply. The result is that renewable energy sources such as wind energy can be accepted when it is available thanks to the presence of an EV battery acting as a buffer on the system. Without the EV battery, the fluctuations in renewable energy supply require that the amount of renewables on the grid be often curtailed, to avoid instability on the electricity system.

This is where energy management comes into play.

Building Energy Management

Similar to the scenario above for EV drivers all arriving home at the same time, buildings such as retail outlets and factory premises can experience peak demands. For a factory, this may correspond with the time when employees arrive to work and start charging their vehicles at the start of the shift.

In this case, the strain may appear on the electrical distribution board feeding the charge points or alternatively, it may cause the company to exceed its Maximum Import Capacity (MIC), the amount of electricity that the building power supply is allowed to consume at any given time.

Currently there are solutions, which monitor the power supply and request the charge points to de-rate or switch off when peak levels are being reached. These solutions require that the installer setup the maximum limits in the software and install current transformers (CT's) on the power supplies.

As an example, let's imagine a car park with 10 charge points each capable of delivering 32 Amps. The board supplying the charge points has 250 Amps available, so we can easily see that the board cannot facilitate all charge points working at full power simultaneously. In this case the first seven vehicles can arrive and start charging, the charge point will deliver 32 Amps per vehicle. When the eighth vehicle arrives, all vehicles may reduce to 25 Amps and when the ninth and tenth vehicle arrives it further reduces to 20 Amps per socket.

By this time, or shortly afterwards, some of the vehicles may have finished charging. In this case the remaining vehicles will be allowed to consume a greater amount proportional to the total power available. The end game is to maximise charging power while facilitating as many vehicles as practical on existing power distribution boards.

A closely related topic within building energy management is the requirement to integrate with a central Building Energy Management System (BEMS). To date, I am not aware of a market ready product that addresses this topic fully, however I see a real need for it. A number of building energy management systems exits, and they are equipped with communications protocols to allow devices to accept orders and send feedbacks. So far, EVSE's have not been integrated into this community, but when they do, the BEMS will be able to control charge, not just in relation to the local distribution panel, but also with the building as a whole. This will allow monitoring of other devices and demand and even scheduling of maximum loads.

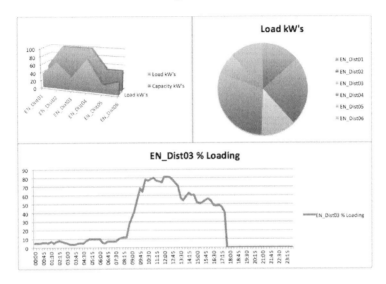

Integrating Renewable Energy

When a building includes some local renewable energy generation such as roof top solar panels, there is an opportunity to match supply with demand. Lets consider a scenario where solar panels are installed on the building and that they have the capability to supply enough energy to charge up to 3 cars. Now lets also consider our previous scenario where you have 10 EV charge points. In this case, with some clever configuration it would be possible to allow all ten vehicles to charge at maximum power without restriction when the solar panels are delivering enough energy.

120

Taking this a step further, if you have battery storage on site, you can adapt your usage to optimise energy production with consumption using the battery as a buffer. This would not have been commercially viable a few years ago, however I believe that with falling costs of both battery and solar power, we are coming very close to a sustainable business model.

Energy Services

The area of energy services is a space with enormous potential. I use the term slightly loosely as I am not speaking just about kWh's but also ancillary services to support voltage and frequency control on the electricity network or grid.

First let me briefly explain a concept called Demand Side Management. Traditionally when the frequency of the electricity transmission system varied, it was brought back to its desired set point by varying the amount of electricity generation in line with the electricity demand. When demand rises the frequency starts to drop, requiring the generation to increase, therefore raising the frequency back to its set point. System operators request generators to raise and lower outputs to facilitate this function.

With the introduction of smart technologies and increased processing power in computer systems, the opportunity has arisen to use the appliances consuming energy to respond to requests, varying energy consumption to help balance the scales between supply and demand. As this method of managing the frequency is carried out at the consumer side of the scales, it is referred to as demand side management.

So lets consider another scenario. Imagine that wind turbines are providing a large percentage of the electricity supply on the grid. As the wind picks up and drops off, the fluctuation in the amount of megawatts (MW's) means that the system frequency is varying and occasionally approaching undesirable levels. In this case the electric vehicles along with other non-essential loads could be interrupted for short periods to assist in controlling the frequency. Moreover, as the electric vehicle has a battery, it holds the potential not only to stop taking power, but also to start taking power when the wind generation is strong.

This is demand side management in operation. If offers a powerful tool to facilitate larger amounts of renewable energy onto our electricity systems while still controlling the system voltages and frequencies.

Control Protocols

As energy management systems need to operate with a range of differing devices from many manufacturers, they communicate through industry standard protocols. In this way there is almost no barrier to the make and model of devices that can be installed in a building for connection to the BEMS.

With the evolution of EV charging technology, similar to other building devices, the charge points will need to adhere to industry protocols when connecting to a BEMS. Up until now, energy management solutions have been limited in functionality and typically executed using proprietary protocols allowing communication only between devices from a single charge point manufacturer. The problem with this approach is that the buyer of the charge points could soon find themselves locked into a vendor forever more. When considering charge points, always check that they are based on open protocols.

Chapter 16

Vehicle To Grid

V2G or Vehicle to Grid is the most commonly used name for what is in fact, a suite of possible applications. V2H (Home) and V2B (Building) are also sometimes used. This chapter will discuss V2X as it relates mainly to the Vehicle to Charge point interface. We will discuss the applications in this chapter, however we will do so separately from the description of the technology. The topic could fill a book completely on its own, so I am only offering an overview here.

What is V2X

V2X is a term that describes the process of feeding energy from the vehicle to one of a number of external users, such as the home, the office building or out to the wider electricity network or grid. The most prominent variation was the notion of sending power back into the electricity grid to ease demand peaks and assist in the resolution of system faults. I say notion because, as yet the applications have been mainly focused on the local area, rather than on a grid scale.

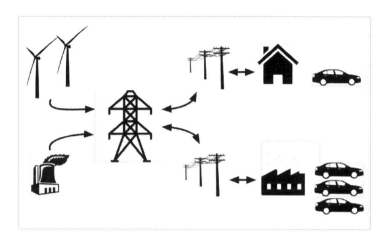

V2X in the Vehicle

Lets start at the car. In the early days vehicles were designed with a battery and a charger. The emphasis was on energy flowing one direction, from the charge point into the vehicle. While considering the impact of electric vehicles on the electricity network, engineers and technologists started to focus on the opportunity which existed from the energy stored in the battery being used for applications, other than propelling the vehicle.

While the battery is much the same in many of the electric vehicles on the market, the ability to send energy back out of the vehicle through the charge point requires some communications and safety protocols. It will also require adjustment of the power electronics to facilitate two-way flow of current.

A growing number of vehicles on offer are now being label as V2G ready. This means that they have implemented the modifications mentioned above and have probably adjusted on-board user displays to allow preference setting.

V2X in the Charge Point

The currently installed charge point network is not really configured for V2X. Furthermore it will probably only be DC charge points which are likely to be set up for V2X anyway. The reason for sticking with DC is that the energy flow is easier to control and also it reduces inefficiencies caused by rectification and regulation of the current.

Despite the lack of V2X devices installed, a number of charge point manufacturers have produced V2X equipment and there are signs that the market for V2G will develop overtime. The devices being developed include an option for integrated battery storage. This can be helpful when looking at balancing energy requirements and buffering the effect on the vehicle battery.

A significant difference between a standard charge point and a V2X charge point, is that the device most incorporate safety features to prevent feeding energy back onto the grid when the local electricity system is de-energized. The purpose of this feature is to avoid electrocution of maintenance staff while they attend to a network fault. Any of you familiar with solar panel systems will be aware of the need for Grid Tie inverters when you are connecting the panels to a building which is in turn connected to the grid. Similar standards are required with V2X systems.

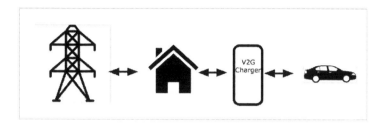

V2X for the Building

For the purpose of discussing the use cases, I will bundle homes, with offices and other buildings. In essence the principles are very similar, where the key objective is the transfer of energy from your vehicle(s) to your building. This use case does not consider exporting energy to the electricity network.

In a V2B situation, there is a relationship between the vehicle owner and the building energy consumer. It might be a family in a home or a staff member at his/her workplace. The vehicle is charged at a convenient time, with the option, that if required, some of the energy is transferred back to the building to help avoid breaching electricity import agreements or possibly provide back-up in the case of a power cut. In the event of a power cut, the building must be able to disconnect itself from the network to avoid danger for maintenance technicians.

One scenario, which has been considered, is the ability to store the energy generated by rooftop solar panels and feed it back to the building during hours of darkness. Another scenario looks at utilizing company EV's to provide a short-term backup supply to the essential services of a building during a power cut. As exporting energy is often at a price less than the cost of importing energy, V2H or V2B may help maximise the return from solar energy by allowing the building to use more of the energy locally rather than exporting it.

V2X for Grid

Similarly to the cases above, I will group the electricity network with the electricity grid. For those of you not familiar there is a differentiation between the Low Voltage '*network*' which distributes the electricity locally and the High Voltage '*grid*' or transmission system which takes power from the big generators and transmits it over large areas before converting the voltages to a level used by consumers.

Much discussion has centred around the notion of using the large numbers of vehicle batteries predicted to be available after mass adoption of EV's, to support the electricity system. This could assist network operators when controlling system voltages or similarly assist transmission operators to control system frequencies, all essential to maintain a good quality electrical system.

In order to facilitate this model, a number of pieces of a jigsaw need to be in place. The charge point must be capable of transferring the power. The communications and protocols need to be in place to allow services to be requested and actioned. Most importantly, a value needs to be agreed on the transaction that can encourage participation of both parties. In reality individual users could not provide the volume that would make the service interesting to the operator, however when large numbers of charge points are aggregated and controlled by one intermediary, they have the potential to offer a valuable service.

When the energy stored in the vehicle, which has previously been paid for is sent back to the grid, the owner will obviously need to be reimbursed. This will require an agreement on the value of the energy (which may be different to what you are buying it for) and it will require energy metering, capable of measuring export as well as import.

The Elephant in the Room

As electric vehicles have developed, there has been debate about the effect of increasing charge-discharge cycles on the health of a battery. Indeed this is a valid question as a key characteristic of a battery is the amount of times it can be cycled and the depth of discharge of the battery.

Newer battery chemistries are far more tolerant of large numbers of cycles, however there still seems to be divided opinion regarding the cost-benefit analysis.

A further consideration is the very practical and immediate topic of State of Charge (SoC) of battery. Lets face it, we are charging the vehicle to use the energy for driving. We have also complained about the limited driving range of early batteries. If we are to export the energy from the vehicle to be used somewhere else, we will still need to ensure we have enough energy to allow us to make the journeys we are already planning. To mitigate against the risk of leaving you short for your journey, you will need to be able to set a minimum level and probably also set a departure time.

Another mitigating factor is the increasing size of the battery. As batteries are getting bigger, it may well be the case, that there is ample capacity to allow you to provide this function and still make your journey.

Balancing the Equation

The cost of a V2X charge point is certain to be significantly greater than that of a basic device. When we consider the potential for using this feature, we should look at factors similar to those below:

- How large is the battery

- How much spare capacity do I regularly have

- Cost of equipment

- Battery health implications

- How often is it utilized

- How much do I receive for kWh's exported

- Is there a fixed fee for providing the service

- Is the electricity supply regularly interrupted

If we can answer these, we should be able to understand whether the V2X function is worthwhile.

Chapter 17

The Sustainable Mobility Triangle

Whether in the workplace or at home, renewable generation in the form of solar panels or wind turbines is becoming far more affordable and far more commonplace. When we generate energy in this way, there are a couple of options of what to do with the energy. Option 1 is to use the energy to power appliances in our own home or building. This has the direct effect of reducing our energy costs by the number of kWh's we managed to avoid importing. Option 2 is to export any energy we don't use powering our appliances back out to the electricity network up stream of the electricity meter. In this case we will need to have a bi directional meter and an agreement from an energy company to pay for this energy, otherwise we see no return on it. Option 3 is that we lose it. Generate energy and lose it, by not using it or getting any monetary return from it.

As I have mentioned in an earlier chapter, there have been significant developments in a number of technologies over the last few years, bringing us to a place of truly sustainable mobility. Moreover, I would argue that they are the catalyst to truly sustainable energy as a whole.

In this chapter we will take a look at what I refer to as the Sustainable Mobility Triangle. This concept looks at the convergence of three technologies that together offer the key to sustainable mobility.

Electric Vehicles

As you may guess from the title of this book, Electric Vehicles are the first side of the triangle. The topic of how EV's have reached maturity has been discussed over various chapters, particularly in the chapter 'Is This Really Happening?' So with no further ado, lets move on to the next technology.

Battery Storage

We don't actually have to move very far, because the next technology is Battery Storage and this is very closely related to the battery in the EV.

Typically battery production was based on the sale of batteries in small sizes. Even though the first principles are the same, the production of larger battery packs is quite a different process to that of the small-scale device.

With the reinvention of electric vehicles, manufacturing plants producing EV batteries are also producing batteries aimed at medium and large-scale energy storage. The Tesla Gigafactory is designed to produce batteries for both electric vehicles and the Tesla Powerwall storage solution. Similarly Nissan offer a storage solution called xStorage. The xStorage solution can be configured with second life batteries from the first generation Nissan Leaf or with new batteries. This configuration option demonstrates the close tie between building storage batteries and EV batteries.

There has always been an interest in battery energy storage, however the cost, lifecycle and maintenance requirements of older battery chemistries has meant that there just wasn't a viable business case. Today however, that business case is coming into focus. The chemistries are far more tolerant, the costs are dropping and they are far less maintenance intensive. All in all, the battery is coming of age.

Solar Energy

The third technology is solar power. In particular I am talking about photovoltaic (PV) or generation of electricity rather than a solar water heating system. I have been looking at this technology for many years and had always been put off by two factors, the cost and the efficiency. OK, so I live in Ireland and Ireland is not known for its abundance of sun. Yes, we have sunny days, it's not always raining, however these sunny days are generally short-lived and the intensity just doesn't match up with southern Europe. When I looked at the expected quantities of power generation from a modest roof top installation, it was less that spectacular. Add to this that the solar generation happened when I was out of the house and not using much energy at home and you can see that the high price of the panels and inverters just didn't stack up. We also didn't have feed-in tariffs for energy sent back onto the grid.

Today however, the picture is changing. Solar panels and inverters are becoming cheaper and more affordable. They have also become more reliable, although you should do a little homework on the type of equipment you are buying. For those of us in northern Europe or similarly sun-deprived areas, there is another development in the solar panels that brightens the future. This is the efficiency of the panels.

Solar panels available today offer higher efficiency than those on sale just a few years ago. For my house, it means that I can generate modest but important amounts of electricity even on a dull day. Moreover, on a winter's day, when the sun is shining, but low in the sky, the panels can produce far more than their predecessors.

But what about my usage profile and being out of the house when the sun is shining? Well, this is where the emergence of all three technologies is coming at the right time. Affordable battery storage means I can now store what I generate until I need it.

Wind generation also holds some possibilities for home use, however the turbines tend to either be very small or else large enough to require planning permissions. For this reason, I will not dwell on it, but rather suggest keeping an eye on where the technology goes.

Time Shifting

Having batteries in your vehicle and in a buffer in your home, mean you can maximize the value of the energy generated at your home. Using what you generate rather than exporting it is far more valuable, as you will rarely if ever receive more for the exported power, than you will pay for importing electricity.

Add to this the possibility of importing off-peak or cheap energy to your battery, for use when you need it during peak times, you may have another opportunity to make savings.

A scenario: You are out of your home, during the day and the sun is shining. At home your solar PV system is merrily transforming those rays to electricity and sending the electricity to the energy storage system in your home. In the early evening, you arrive home when you wish to cook, have a shower and recharge your vehicle. The energy storage system now sends the home-generated energy out to the vehicle and other appliances requiring power. During the night, electricity from your energy provider is cheaper than in the daytime, so your battery tops up by enough to get you through the morning peak, when breakfasts are prepared and showers are taken. All before the sun shines on the solar panels. As you leave the house, the sun shines and starts to bring your battery pack back to full before you arrive home again.

Optimising the Battery Size
When installing such a system as described above, we will need to avoid wastage. Installing too much storage or generation capacity means spending money on a resource that we will not utilise to its full potential. The key to unlocking the correct configuration is in understanding our usage patterns.

First we need to examine the amount of energy we use to commute each day. This will be combined with the size of battery installed in our vehicle. We will then need to consider the amount of energy used in the house and the time of day this energy is required.

Once we understand these factors we can start to look at what generation capacity we wish to install and what home storage battery size is optimum to ensure maximum return. The sweet spot is where you will use all of a particular resource all the time or almost all the time. If you are purchasing based on occasional peaks in usage, you are probably wasting money. Do however look a little into the future and at least allow for any potential expansion as your usage profile adapts and technology costs change.

Beyond Mobility

As you can see from the scenario described above, the sustainability opportunity, which revolves around EV's, solar panels and energy storage, goes beyond simply putting power in your electric vehicle. The combination of these technologies offers the potential for using renewable and distributed sources of energy for a growing number of consumers. Having the ability to store energy in an economical way means we can become less dependent on fossil fuel power stations and more self-sufficient. While I understand that this impacts on the business models and sustainability of the electricity transmission systems, I also believe that the transition will be a gradual one and therefore allow a relatively smooth migration to a micro-grid world. The real challenge here lies with the energy regulators who guide the industry to facilitate the most efficient, sustainable and secure electricity for energy users.

Return on Investment

Having set out all the advantages and opportunities above, it still boils down to 'brass tacks'…. money. In most cases in life, it is easier and cheaper to design solutions for larger use cases than it is for a domestic scenario. This is because the economies of scale mean that the return on investment pays dividend earlier.

On this occasion, it is possible that the small energy consumer may be in pole position. Large energy consumers typically pay far less for the energy they consume than the domestic consumer. In many cases this is close to half the rate per kWh. As the cost of energy is low, the potential for savings is reduced also.

In the case of the domestic situation, the higher cost of energy means each kWh and each day that passes is providing close to double the payback. Thus reducing the time before a cost becomes a profit.

Chapter 18

A Look At Commercial Vehicles

Electric Vehicles in fleets are seen as attractive propositions by many. Up until recently however, there have been a few obstacles in the way of widespread adoption. Some fleet managers may bypass any real consideration of electric vehicles when they perceive additional effort and risk. Much of this perception stems from a lack of understanding of the technology and certainly many fleet managers are finding themselves outside their comfort zone.

Sooner or later we won't be able to just ignore the arrival of e-Mobility, however by that time, many of the early benefits such as grants and tax relief will have started to fade. We are currently at a sweet spot, where we can't really be called early adopters but on the other hand there are still incentives. Importantly the risks associated with early adoption have diminished.

Commerce and the sustainability of electric vehicles in business depends on EV's being able to carry out the required functions without impacting negatively on the customer experience and the overall cost of operating the business. Fuel costs and maintenance costs are seen as no-brainers, so what's the problem.

Early adopters were introduced to conversion vehicles, where a commonplace and respected brand of combustion engine vehicle was taken by a third party and converted to an electric power train. Many of the experiences of these early adopters were less than satisfactory. Limited availability of trained technicians meant that any repair or maintenance work was often substantially more expensive than the combustion engine equivalent. Moreover the vehicles tended to lack uniformity, using similar but not identical components across vehicles of the same vintage, thus introducing unnecessary complication when carrying out repairs.

The further issue of battery management exposed some users to problems where vehicles would show erratic feedback of state of charge and sometimes end up running out of charge with little warning. Battery chemistry sometimes added to the problem as some early vehicles used very maintenance intensive batteries before lithium-ion batteries became more affordable. All in all this chapter of the evolution was often not the most positive.

The next generation saw traditional car companies produce vehicles in line with the processes used for their combustion engine fleet. These vehicles tended to be far more reliable, however an eagerness to have the vehicles adopted by high profile clients has in some cases caused vehicles to be sold into unsuitable use cases. As early production vehicles suffered from limited range and a lack of fast recharging features, users often found that while they performed sufficiently in some conditions and at some times of year, they often came up short at other times. As the recharge time was relatively long, topping up the vehicle was not practical.

In more recent times, the range of commercial vehicles on offer has increased. Vans and trucks are available in an increasing range of sizes and configurations. From 1 tonne panel vans to 10 tonne rigid curtain siders, the choice is growing. However the important factor from my perspective is that the battery sizes are now increasing and fast charging technology has been introduced. Older models were often limited to battery sizes similar to those in small passenger cars. Today, there are vans with larger batteries and more practical driving ranges.

A significant benefit stemming from the participation of the traditional vehicle manufacturers was a gradual increase in the number of trained technicians who could competently carry out works including the disconnection and removal of large battery packs. These battery packs come with so many danger notices, that the traditional mechanic was left in no doubt, that they shouldn't touch them. Today most brands have a network of technicians in almost all regions, capable of completing any required works.

As the newer offerings have introduced fast

charging, there is also the opportunity to increase the daily driving range of the vehicle by utilising natural breaks in the day to refuel the vehicle. In many cases, this may not be absolutely necessary, however it certainly offers a level of confidence and comfort when deciding to drive electric.

Maintenance

Maintaining an electric vehicle is notoriously inexpensive. No engine oils, and fewer moving parts are regularly mentioned. This is of course true, however it's not the end of the story. Braking systems in an electric vehicle utilise a combination of regenerative braking (using the motor to slow down the vehicle) and friction braking (brake pads & disks). As the driver lightens the pressure of their foot on the accelerator or presses on the brake, the vehicle controls initially use regenerative braking to slow the vehicle while feeding energy back into the battery. It is only in the latter stages of braking that friction braking is required, therefore the requirement to replace brake pads, is much reduced over that of a combustion engine vehicle.

There is also an argument that tyres wear less on an electric vehicle. The theory is that the 'Eco' mode of many vehicles, decreases the acceleration from stop and reduced the wear on tyres. My experience of tyre wear has been very good (over 60,000km on a set of tyres). While it certainly augers well, I cannot proclaim to having enough hard evidence to call this a trend.

Fuel costs

One of the major budget considerations for any fleet manager is fuel cost. Prices of diesel rise and fall, but in the long run, they really only increase. Anything a fleet manager can do to reduce fuel costs will be significant in the end of year budget.

For this reason electric vehicles, if they suit your driving needs, are a big win item. Typically the cost of refuelling an EV can be in the region of 20-30% of the diesel equivalent. As most regions operate a 'peak' and 'off peak' meter, organisations may benefit from charging 'off peak', typically half the price of peak rates. In this case ensure the vehicle is equipped with a timer to facilitate scheduling.

Charging Home or Away

When considering opportunities to charge a fleet of electric vehicles, there are three main areas to keep in mind.

Depot Charging

Charging back at base is probably the simplest solution. Vehicles can have dedicated charge points and parking spaces. Scheduling can take place to spread the peak-charging load or simply to avail of 'off-peak' energy prices. Another benefit of charging at the depot is that commercial properties tend to have larger power supply connections than domestic premises. Therefore, charging at 32 Amps is more likely to be feasible. Energy prices at the depot are also a known factor and therefore are easier to predict.

Charging on the Go

While a vehicle is out and about during the working day, it may have opportunities to charge. Whether using fast chargers or normal 'on-street' chargers, this will require an account or subscription with a service provider.

Energy costs on street may be more expensive than at the depot, particularly if you are using 'off-peak' rates when you are back at base. However for small top ups or as a way to turn a borderline application into a comfortable one, it may still be worthwhile.

Depending on the options available in the locations that suit you, you may be able to avail of standard or fast charging. Typically fast charging will come at a small premium.

Charging at Home

In some cases, you may be able to arrange for drivers to charge the vehicles at home. This would be of particular interest where the driver normally takes the vehicle home at night. In this case, you will need to consider the energy costs. A charge point installed at the drivers home which included a power meter and communications would allow the energy to be monitored and reimbursed.

Grants and Tax Breaks

When considering purchasing electric vehicles for fleets, you should investigate what tax breaks and grants are available locally. In some regions, the cost of electric vehicles and charge points may be written down against profits over a very short time period. Purchase grants may also be available, which would reduce the starting price.

Total Cost of Ownership

When we do look at electric vehicle in fleets their is a risk, that we will only consider the price tag. We should be looking at the Total Cost of Ownership (TCO). TCO should include:

Purchase Price

Purchase Grants

Tax Reliefs

Fuel Costs

Maintenance Costs

Road & Registration Tax

Insurance Costs

Purchase prices have dropped considerably over the last couple of years. They are however still more expensive than a diesel engine vehicle. Where a region has a rebate or grants system, the cost is now brought a little closer to par. Tax reliefs can now bring you right in line. At this point you can start to see real savings on Fuel costs and also on maintenance. With an emphasis on reducing emissions, road tax or its equivalent is often cheaper for EV's than combustion engines. However when it comes to insurance, regions differ hugely. Some countries are experiencing approximately equal insurance costs, while others are lower and more still are higher.

Understanding your Needs

If your fleet is equipped with vehicle tracking, you are in a great place to understand what you need from an EV. You can easily decipher the distance requirements as well as the time parked and opportunities for topping up during the day. With all this information at hand, you can start to look at suitably sized vehicles and hone in on those with sufficient driving range. However here lies the trap. Be sure to acquire good quality information on the true and real life driving ranges of the vehicles. Standard drive cycles used to assess vehicles and provide brochure information just don't reflect real life.

Chapter 19

The Business Of Electric Mobility

Electric vehicles and e-Mobility make a fascinating business topic. Starting at the level of Governments, there is often a split of responsibility between Energy, Transport and even Environment. Automotive manufacturers see electric vehicles as a natural evolution from the fossil fuel vehicles they sell today and electricity utilities focus on the new type of consumer arriving just in time to take up the demand slump from energy efficient appliances. The business of electric mobility has gathered an eclectic mix of players, each determined to take a slice of the action. The hustle for business filters down into all sorts of areas and some of the interested parties are new to both the transport and energy sectors.

One point that seems very obvious to me is that some of the larger players have shown a determination to hold on to traditional methods of doing business. This steadfast approach probably equates to building the barricades to deter new entrants from entering the marketplace. Innovation is somewhat stifled by the lack of willingness to invite newbies into the circle. This is not to say that innovation isn't happening at all. It is... and some of it is mind-blowing.

As with many aspects of today's way of doing business, communications and ICT are two of the prominent enablers to opening up opportunities. In the electric vehicle world they facilitate the transport and presentation of data from vehicles, charge points and smart phones all over the world.

As I attempt to give you a taste for the many flavours of the e-Mobility Business, I will try to look at them from the point of view of the key stakeholders.

Vehicle Manufacturers

Probably a good place to start. The vehicle manufacturer, as with most organisations is always assessing the marketplace, looking for new opportunities to grow both market share and profits. The introduction of electric vehicles, takes them at least temporarily, out of the efficient high-volume manufacturing regime they have been accustomed to. This development means additional costs and logically, additional corporate pressure to recoup and capitalise on the investment.

With the introduction of greater levels of communications within the vehicle, as well as the proliferation of smartphones, the car company is in a good position to take ownership of the customers' entire mobility experience. They can offer a range of services on the back of the technologies installed in the vehicles. Data from the vehicle can contribute to growth in service-centre revenue through introduction of push notifications or alternatively it can inform business models for inclusive maintenance packages.

Some of the manufacturers have started to offer free electricity at public charging infrastructure. Contracts between car companies and electricity providers have even facilitated the issue of "Green Energy Certificates". If I take this a step further and look at the area of energy storage and renewable generation, it seems that soon enough the vehicle manufacturer may want to cross over the fence and start providing energy services to the home. After all they have batteries and some even have solar companies.

Another emerging trend in mobility is the growth of car sharing schemes. This migration from individual ownership of vehicles will impact the way vehicle manufacturers do business. A strategy of offering Mobility as a Service (MaaS), would position the car companies well, to maintain market share.

The Electricity Company

The Utility sector itself has gone through immense change over the last couple of decades. Where traditionally, the utilities were state owned, incorporating the full scope of generation, distribution and retail, regulation of the industry has moved utilities into competitive markets. The battle for market share will encourage electricity retailers to search for new customers and this will extend to new ways of consuming electricity.

Depending on what part of the electricity system they operate in, the company may have a different focus. The priorities of an electrical generation company will be different to those of the supply or retail company. The distribution and transmission operators will also have independent viewpoints.

The commercial possibilities in the e-Mobility domain are far and wide. Provision of energy and provision of energy related services are just two and these are the areas I will focus on.

Electric vehicle users will require electricity to fuel their vehicles. At home this may be straight forward, however on the public infrastructure, the driver, doesn't own the energy meter. Energy retailers are already actively selling energy to both domestic and commercial customers. The next logical migration is to either sell energy directly to the end user from publically available charging infrastructure or to sell the energy to the EV service providers who operate charge points.

Energy related services on the other hand offer the potential for the retailers to generate revenue from the provision of services to the electricity system operators, through controlling the energy demand of end users. In other chapters we have talked about energy services, this is where it can come into operation. A retailer could offer to reduce system demand in reaction to a drop in frequency or even increase demand where the frequency rises. Similarly the retailer could control consumption to assist the distribution operator in the control of voltage.

Fuel Forecourt Operator

Before we adopt the electricity company as our provider of fuel, lets not forget the traditional fuel forecourt and motorway service operator. These entities are also under pressure to maintain and grow market share. As with the utility, they two have undergone significant change. In this case, the pressures of fuel margins, has meant that most forecourt operators see themselves as forecourt retailers rather than 'petrol companies'. As fuel margins have reduced, the business model has adapted to grow revenue in the areas of food, newspapers, light refreshments and even laundry services.

Electric vehicles cannot be ignored, particularly when forecourt operators are conscious that the customer arrives on wheels. While EV users are charging their vehicles, they represent a captive audience. Just as with gasoline, the margin on electricity is low, however there is a multitude of other ways to generate income or optimise the margin.

Charge Point Operators

The operation of charge points is a growing business. In the end, some of the operators will be dominant for years to come, while cash rich companies determined to keep a grip on fuel provision will acquire others.

In order to survive, the operator will need to maximise the income generated through the operation of the charge points. As mentioned, the margin on electricity is small; therefore other revenue streams will need to expand to make the proposition attractive. Similar to the electricity retailers, the EVSE operator may look to provide system support services. This would become attractive when the number of simultaneous users on the infrastructure grows.

Another area of interest is advertising. I can see three main streams of advertising. Firstly, the charge point is a static device, which can be branded to advertise third party products. A second possibility is advertising through the user interface screen on the charge point, this could target products and services directly to the known user. Finally when accessing payment accounts on smartphones or computers, advertising can be presented to the user.

The Aggregator

When we look at the way disruptive business models have infiltrated many industries, we should also consider that the obvious participants in eMobility would not just be the traditional players. Most of the commercial opportunity comes from the operation of volume. As an individual, I cannot trade energy or provide energy services, but if an aggregator comes along who can pool the resource, then the proposition is attractive.

But who are these aggregators? They can come from the traditional players, however, knowledge is power and the buzz is 'Data Mining'. The guys who can generate the algorithms are the ones who potentially could control the services market. Just consider: the search engine company is really a large marketing company and some of them are already active in the autonomous vehicle space. Maybe my electricity or e-Mobility services will come from an Internet company.

SaaS Developers

Software as a Service is a growing part of business today. As mentioned above, data mining and algorithms are all part of the way we are starting to do business and e-Mobility is no different. However as small or dispersed businesses, we may find it hard to find the resources to develop all the code required to build our revenue. This is where third party SaaS providers can come to the rescue. The software is developed based on a large and dispersed market and provided as a solution to e-Mobility operators for a monthly fee.

Dividing the Pie

In the end, the business will be divided, with some participants happy to take a modest share, while others attempt to take a lion's share. We are likely to see companies diversifying their employee base, to skill up for the future. Others will look to form strategic partnerships as a way to ensure survival.

Building a strategic partnership will require gaining comfort that your partner, doesn't want to eat your slice of the pie. Any company entering such an arrangement will need to protect their business both through legal contract and also by analysing the growth interests of the proposed partner.

The End User

The end user should not be forgotten in all this talk about commerce. In the end, these are the ones who will pay the piper. As discussed previously the list of potential end users could be very long, when you have considered all the aspects of the e-Mobility business. However lets take a short look at the EV driver.

Charging the vehicle is the most obvious business transaction that can be expected to take place. As we know from other activities, users differ and their preferences vary also. Lets take a look at the mobile phone market for some guidance.

While early offerings of EV charging services have opted for one metric or another as a means of doing business, the evolution of the industry is likely to see more choice for the customer. Telecoms operators tend to offer a variety of packages to users, including 'Bill-Pay', 'Pay-as-You-Go' and bundled monthly subscriptions. As the technology matures, the EV domain will need to adopt similar offerings and no doubt these services will be fine-tuned as the market grows.

One final consideration regarding the end user is their willingness or lack thereof, to allow service companies to control the way they charge and discharge their vehicle. If service providers wish to start or stop charge events, they customer will need two things. They will need comfort that they will still have the ability to use their vehicle when they want and they will also want to see some benefit, either financial or otherwise for provision of the service. Quality of Service (QoS) agreements are likely to be a significant part of any sustainable arrangement.

Chapter 20

So You've Got A Big Idea!

Many great ideas have been developed during the recent evolution of electric vehicle and associated products & services. However as I have stated previously, this evolution is still underway. We need no better example of possibilities than to go back to the advent of mobile telephones and consider where the journey has taken us thus far.

Developments in the electric vehicle arena have come in many forms. They have spanned from battery technology, to charging equipment, mobile phone applications and even to electricity network support technology. As the migration to EV's continues, there will be obstacles and opportunities, which will be addressed by clever thinkers.

Coming up with an Idea

If you don't actually have an idea yet, but would like to work on one, then my advice is work on something that is closely fitted with your area of expertise. If you are an electronics designer, then look at ideas in this area, similarly, if your talent is mobile phone applications, then that's where you should stay. I am not saying that there is no room for collaboration, on the contrary. But do approach the search from your home expertise.

Another good trick is to approach from the point of view of a need or problem. Has someone a need or a problem to solve? Maybe that some one is the EV driver, maybe it is the company owner, or even the electricity supplier. Don't limit yourself to the driver of the vehicle, you should also think in the wider sphere. Once the light bulbs start to shine brighter in your head, you may find the possibilities are endless.

I have the idea, what next?

As I am sure you will already know, coming up with the idea is just the start of the process. Now lets look at what comes next.

Background checking is all-important. Just because you haven't heard of a particular idea, it doesn't mean, someone hasn't already developed it. Do a search of the Internet with keywords that might help you uncover any previous work. Remember you may not find it on page 1 or 2 of the search results. Be prepared to dig deep. If this hasn't found anything you may want to try to conduct a patent search, although this is not for the faint hearted. There is also the possibility that the idea was attempted but failed. In this case you need to identify why and whether your solution is better.

Does the problem exist? This is always a good check to do early on. Sometimes a problem is only a problem until you look at the real life situation. I have come across many solutions to problems that EV drivers don't actually experience, or at least not typically. If you do identify that the problem is real, have a look into other industries and see if the same problem exists and how it has been addressed. You should also consider if the problem is a short-term issue, maybe imminent progress such as the speed of charging or the size of the battery will relegate the problem into history.

Test your Idea to check it holds water so to speak. No offense, but just because you have an idea, doesn't mean it's a good one. I have the pleasure of regular interactions with engineers much more clever than myself, however sometimes, these clever guys and girls mistake a clever technical achievement with a solution. For a start, the problem must be real, and then the solution must be practical and affordable. Just because the solution is technically

155

perfect or even brilliant, doesn't mean it is what the intended user wants or will pay for.

Commerce is always important. No matter how good an idea you have, if it can't be developed at a reasonable price point, it won't float. Remember that the cost of the product can't be greater than the perceived gain to user. I say perceived gain, because it may not be simply monetary value. Sometimes the value to the customer comes in another form, maybe convenience. In this case, you will need to put a realistic value on the convenience and be happy that the customer will pay for it. I use a catch phrase "You can't have sustainable energy or sustainable mobility without sustainable business". What I mean by this is simple, if there isn't value for both the buyer and the seller, the business won't last and the product or service will die.

Solo or Partnership is a decision to be made. There are a number of factors to the making and the timing of that decision. Can you develop the idea all on your own or will you need help? This help could be technical or financial. Once developed, the idea may need to get into a seasoned distribution network. If you are looking at venture capitalists, they won't just be interested in one good solution, they will want a whole suite of products, recurring revenue, your soul, your organs and anything else they can get. OK, this may be a little exaggeration, however they will want more than a single point of revenue.

Patents are important for a number of reasons. You should always consider a Non-Disclosure Agreement (NDA) before you divulge any of your secret sauce, however once you have an idea sufficiently fleshed out, you should also try to obtain a patent for it. If the idea can't be patented for some reason, you better be fast at making a return. It won't be long before the vultures come in to eat your lunch.

Knowing *Who is the 'go to' Entity,* is important. I have seen many good ideas getting a cold reception, because the proposer was talking to the wrong person. For example, talking to the car manufacturer with a solution to a problem that the electricity company is experiencing is not going to get you very far. I understand that this example may seem very obvious, however depending on your idea; a subtle change in direction may get you a lot further. Once you are confident you are talking to the correct person, they will often provide the strongest indication of the value of your idea.

Listen to the intended customer. Sometimes you will have an idea, but the greatest value from the idea may be something you haven't thought of. Often the intended customer will spot other values and ideas that their area of expertise can identify. They just don't have your solution.

Don't Try Too Hard. Many of the companies and individuals I have worked with, try to solve all the worlds, or at least the EV problems in one go. When we remember the old adage, that you "Can't please all the people all the time", there is a hint there for everyone. Take your good idea and focus it, so that you solve one problem or create one opportunity really well. If you have other ideas, store them until the first is properly fleshed out. It is so easy to get carried away, falling into the project creep trap. Having warned you to control your enthusiasm, I would balance this by suggesting that if your multiple ideas are interlinked, you will need to leave space in the master design to add modules later. Plan ahead, don't build ahead!

Chapter 21

Will EV's Cause Grid Meltdown?

The Simple answer to this question is NO!

I never cease to be amazed as article after article is published, each telling the general public that the uptake of Electric Vehicles will cause Grid Meltdown. Many of the articles even quote energy regulators and grid operators. So why, if its not true, are these articles appearing with such frequency?

There are a few potential reasons. Bias, ignorance and laziness are on the top of the list of these reasons.

It is said, "paper never refuses ink". In this modern electronic era, the old adage is just as true as it was before the Internet. In some cases, the one composing the article has a bias towards a particular technology and against electric vehicles. In other cases the person is writing without committing to sufficient research and uncovering the true facts. Some think that reading the headline or by-line of an article is sufficient to justify repeating a claim without giving the rest of the story.

In these days of shock journalism, it seems also that it is more important to have a strong and controversial headline that one that reflects the true facts of the article. A case in point is a headline, which proclaimed, "National Grid, Electric Vehicles will cause Grid Meltdown". This article appeared on a number of media sources with varied wording on the same subtext. The article even referenced the report from which the claim was extracted. Naturally I was shocked, so off I went to read the specified report. What I found was that the National Grid in question, considered a number of different scenarios around the uptake of electric vehicles and the impact they might have on the grid. The scenarios, ranged from slow uptake over a long period, to massive uptake overnight. Somewhere in the middle they described the more likely migration process.

On top of the migration to EV's they also considered what technologies and solutions existed or were under development to assist with any perceived stresses caused by EV's on the grid. Only in the extreme scenario of massive and almost immediate uptake of EV's combined with an absence of technology and business solutions, would the grid be at risk of melting down. Their more reasonable conclusion was that the uptake would be more gradual and that solutions could be in place before the levels become unmanageable.

The time of mass migration to electrification of transport has been long awaited. While it is certainly picking up momentum and I believe inevitable, it will not happen over night. During all the time of developing the vehicle technology, there has been similar effort put into developing complimentary technologies, which provide solutions to problems as well as opportunities for mutual benefit. I know because I was involved in the development of some of these solutions, which have now become full blown commercially available products. Apart from those I have been directly involved with, I am also familiar with the work of many others who share a vision of the future opportunities.

A more gradual uptake will allow industry to meet the challenges, which demand presents. From time to time during this evolution, there will be pinch points where supply is slower than desired. These are more likely to be minor inconveniences that critical losses.

I must acknowledge that not all countries have developed equally when it comes to electricity networks. These countries are under strain even now, due to substandard networks, being barely able to cope with the existing demand. These counties would struggle with a mass uptake of EV's, however if the economy of the consumers can handle a migration to EV's, then they should be able to handle upgrading the supply network. There is even an argument that battery storage may offer part of the solution.

The world doesn't operate on a level playing field. It should be acknowledged that the poorer countries are often treated like the rubbish heaps for the more prosperous ones. However I was amazed to visit one such country recently, only to be greeted by large numbers of PEV's in the most unlikely of cities.

There are organisations that provide financing to governments and industry to integrate clean and accessible energy solutions to underdeveloped countries. I would encourage industry to see where they can do some real good, while all the time developing a market for their products.

Chapter 22

A Look At What The Future Holds

Writing about what the future has in store is like looking into a crystal ball. I don't want to compare myself to a less than genuine fortune-teller, however I have to admit using a similar technique. When I want to see what the future may hold, I look at what I see in front of me and I assess what I know of the past.

The lessons learned both in the electric vehicle industry and across other industries, may give indications towards the path ahead. As I have alluded to previously, "Money Makes The World Go Round" and therefore we should expect that the developments of the future while driven by a variety of goals, will be sustained by successful business.

Light posts

There has been much discussion about integrating charge points into light posts. However this is not as simple as many seem to think. Lighting standards are often configured to an earthing arrangement, which is not compatible with charge point standards. The earthing at each of the light posts would need to be upgraded to make them compatible. On top of this the amount of power available is limited by two other factors: the cable size and the circuit calculations. The cable size could typically carry enough of current for a 16 Amp (3.6kW) charge in addition to the load from the lights themselves. However an even greater restriction is the circuit calculation for the supply feeding a street of light posts. The circuit load is calculated based on a current draw of approximately 6 Amps per lighting standard.

This would mean that a street of 10 light poles might supply a maximum of 60 Amps. Allowing for reduced loads due to the introduction of more efficient L.E.D. lighting, the available surplus power is likely to be about 32 Amps or two 16 Amp sockets, from a street of ten light poles. As battery sizes are increasing this charge rate is likely to be completely inadequate to meet user requirements.

In practice I see this panning out a little different. When a charge point manufacturer is designing the charge point of the future, they are likely to consider other functions within the device. One function could be a data or Wi-Fi hot spot, particularly as the charge points have communications installed anyway, however another could be an integrated lighting standard. In this case the electric installation will be cognisant of the overall loads right from the point of design.

Battery Size

I have mentioned earlier, that not everyone needs a large battery in his or her EV and that carrying around underutilised battery capacity is both inefficient and costly. For this reason, I think that in a similar way to the way vehicles are divided into size categories, there will also be a grouping of battery sizes. The battery size groupings and the vehicle size groupings will probably be interlinked, as larger vehicles may dictate larger size batteries.

As battery costs fall, as well as any gains from improved energy density, the smallest size of battery available will almost certainly rise from the levels of today. This will be a gradual evolution and is not likely to cause any devaluation of the current EV stock. The likely groupings of battery will start at 30kWh, heading next to 60kWh, 90kWh, 120kWh and so on. The specific sizes are likely to be dictated by packaging configurations. Smaller vehicles will come with smaller options while large vehicles will come with larger options. All this is quite similar to the way, engine sizes are offered at the moment. You will rarely see a

2-litre engine in a city car, just like you will rarely see a larger size vehicle with a small engine.

Vehicle Power Intake

Currently vehicles are offered with AC charging and DC charging, typically divided by the rate of charge. On the DC side, Europe is adopting CCS and it seems certain now that the manufacturers currently using the CHAdeMO specification will migrate to CCS in the very near future.

AC charging is presently facilitated with the installation of 'On-Board' chargers ranging in size from 3kW up to 22kW. Few new models of vehicle are now being offered with 3kW as it is seen as insufficient for the newer generation battery sizes. Batteries would simply take too long to charge. 7kW has been adopted as the baseline for vehicles being delivered today. 11kW and 22kW require the vehicle to have a 3-phase 'On-Board' charger. This adds cost and weight to the vehicle, which is never desirable from an auto manufacturers point of view.

For this reason and tied to the next point on public or destination charging, I believe we will see a simplification of offerings. AC will be limited to single phase with a maximum charge rate of approximately 10kW, while DC (CCS) will allow charging all the way to the maximum value of the vehicle. Larger battery sizes will be capable of 350kW charging while smaller batteries may have an upper limit anywhere from 50kW to 150kW

On-street or Destination Charging

Currently this type of charging tends to come in the form of AC charging. 7, 11 or 22kW. For the next few years these formats are likely to form the backbone of On-street charging. However this technology has a drawback; it is very often underutilised. I don't mean the number of charge events; these will increase as the number of vehicles increases. Instead I am focusing on one of the elements of the business model that will sustain EV charging infrastructure installation; kWh's. More kWh's supplied to a vehicle while charging, adds to the revenue that the charge point can generate. Presently the vast majority of vehicles on the roads cannot accept 22kW, those limiting the kWh's per time interval.

My crystal ball shows a gradual migration to DC (CCS) charging at these locations typically delivering 20kW per outlet. These charge points will cost the installer more to purchase, however the revenue they can generate will justify this additional cost. Drivers will be happier, as they will be able to take greater amounts of energy on board, even with relatively short stops. Additionally the communications protocols available in CCS charging will open up other revenue streams for the operator.

Fast/Rapid Charging
The adoption of CCS as a standard in Europe will pave the way to a more valuable charging experience for many of the industry stakeholders. 350kW charging on Motorways and intercity routes can be facilitated through the same connector as 50kW and below in urban areas and even on the streets. As CCS incorporates the ISO/IEC15118 Vehicle to Grid Standard, the possibilities for communication between car and electrical network are numerous. Charge point operators will be able to offer services to the electricity distribution or transmission companies, while at the same time maximising the energy transfer through the charge point.

The driver will benefit through more efficient charging experiences. Opportunities while shopping or going to an appointment will gain value, while intercity driving will become far more practical with fewer and shorter stops on long distance journeys.

Home Charging

This is an area where my crystal ball shows a slightly more off the wall image. Charging at home is presently facilitated with an AC charge point, furthermore the charge rates are by necessity quite low. Doing smart things with an AC charger is a little clunky, as the protocols are quite restrictive. This restricts the possible functionality of the hardware or more accurately increases the cost of hardware to facilitate the smarts.

If we look at our TV service, we may remember the evolution from the set top antenna to a cable network and then to a set top box, which added functionality. The set top box is normally supplied as part of a contract. Sign up for 12 or 24 months and the cable company will give you a fancy box. This same model is used from Internet services to Cell phones.

The home charge point may similarly evolve. It will migrate to a DC charging format, allowing a variable charge rate of up to around 10 or 12kW. An energy service provider will provide the charge point free of charge with for example, a 24-month contract. This service provider may be your electricity supply company or it might even be a separate service company. The charge point will facilitate a more flexible integration with home energy storage systems and local renewable electricity generation.

Autonomous Vehicles

Did you really think I could finish this book without mentioning autonomous vehicles? Of course not!

Electric vehicles contain many of the technical qualities required for autonomous vehicles. Amongst other things, these qualities relate to the transmission system and the fuel system.

Electric vehicles are based on automatic transmission. Some will argue that there is no transmission, but the point is, there is no clutch and gear mechanism, therefore it is already equipped for a smooth, linear movement from stop to full speed and back to stop. The fly by wire technology already integrated into electric vehicles is essentially the same as that required in the autonomous vehicle.

Because EV's are fuelled from electricity the refuelling options required for an autonomous vehicle is already half way there. It is clean, and efficient and it won't leak all over the ground. On top of this, technologies such as inductive charging will allow vehicles to position themselves over charge pads and accept a charge while at rest.

Current versions of electric vehicles already contain many of the features we might expect from the autonomous car. Lane departure warnings and correction systems are now becoming standard. Intelligent cruise control including automatic overtake and distance adjust are also in some of the new models. The technology that will enable autonomous vehicles is already here and much of it exists in the EV. The challenges ahead for the self-drive car are likely to be more regulatory and commercial, than technical.

In truth a chapter on what the future holds is a recipe for failure. On one side, should one of the predictions fail to materialise, you can say I was wrong. On the other hand, even if all predictions come through, the future of EV's is likely to produce some far more fascinating developments.

Happy & Safe Motoring!

"You may doubt the distance capability of an Electric Vehicle, but never underestimate the energy of an EV driver as they debate the virtues of electric vehicles, for hours and hours and hours and hours......."

Printed in Germany
by Amazon Distribution
GmbH, Leipzig